# Winter in Finland

A Study in Human Geography

*by W. R. Mead*

*and Helmer Smeds*

FREDERICK A. PRAEGER, *Publishers*

New York · Washington

BOOKS THAT MATTER

Published in the United States of America in 1967
by Frederick A. Praeger, Inc., Publishers
111 Fourth Avenue, New York, N.Y. 10003

Library of Congress Catalog Card Number 67–27404

Printed in the Republic of Ireland

# Contents

Foreword p. 11   Maps and Diagrams p. 9   Illustrations p. 7

PART 1 THE PROBLEM, ITS CAUSES AND EFFECTS

*Chapter 1 The Nature of the Problem*
Frostiana p. 14   The Singularity of the Experience p. 15   The Legend of Winter p. 16.   The Record of the Facts p. 21   The Language of Winter p. 24   Finland and the Winter Freeze p. 25

*Chapter 2 Causes and Effects*
A Definition of Winter p. 29   A Question of Latitude p. 30   The Advance and Retreat of the Snow Frontier p. 37   The Advance and Retreat of the Ice Frontier p. 39   (a) Ice and the Inland Waters p. 39   (b) Frost in the Ground p. 41   (c) Ice and the Surrounding Seas p. 43   The Silhouette of Finland p. 48

PART 2 SOLUTIONS TO THE PROBLEM

*Chapter 3 The Assault on Winter*
(a) *The Struggle with Ice* p. 52   The Birth of Winter Shipping p. 52   Broadening the Base of Winter Shipping p. 55   The Growth of the Icebreaker Fleet p. 57   Development of Icebreaker Construction p. 57   The Function and Structure of Icebreakers p. 60   The Development of Ice Forecasting p. 61   The Deployment of the Icebreaker Fleet p. 63   The Consequences of the Assault on Winter Icing p. 69   The Use of Ice Thawing Techniques p. 70   (b) *The Obstruction of Snow* p. 71   Snow and National Communications p. 71   Snow in an Urban Context p. 74   The Problem of the Thaw p. 76   (c) *Light in the Darkness* p. 78   Breaking Winter's Siege p. 82

*Chapter 4 Refuge from the Winter*
Migration and Hibernation p. 85   Designs for Living p. 88   The Problem of Heating p. 89   Winter Building p. 92   Fashions in Clothing p. 95   Food for Energy p. 97   A Matter of Acclimitisation p. 98

*Chapter 5 The Exploitation of Winter*
The Time of the Runner p. 101   The Art of Hunting p. 102   The Role of the Sledge p. 105   The Place of the Ski p. 109   The Birth of Winter Sports p. 112   A Season of Sociability p. 115   The Nature of Lumbering p. 117   The Virtues of the Winter Circumstance p. 119

*Chapter 6 The Balance Sheet of Winter*
The Changing Character of Winter p. 122   The Changing Approach to Winter p. 125   Winter in the Seasonal Rhythm of Activity p. 127   Winter in Summer p. 134   The Triumph of Summer p. 138   A Bill for Winter p. 139

# Illustrations

1. *Helsinki in Winter* (by P. Gaimard).
2. A Laplander descending a mountain on his snow skates.
3. A Journey through Åland's pack ice.
4. Aurora borealis.
5. *Halla* (by Hugo Simberg).
6. Street in Helsinki on a winter morning.
7. March in North Finland.
8. *Voima*, one of Finland's larger icebreakers.
9. An ice hole fisherman.
10. A boy in a blizzard in front of the University Library, Helsinki.
11. One of the 600,000 lorry loads of snow which must be deposited in Helsinki bay in an average winter.
12. Horse transport of logs.
13. A building under construction with its protective covering against low temperature.
14. South Harbour, Helsinki, during March.
15. The army stands at ease.
16. A children's ice hill.

# Maps and Diagrams

Figure  1.  Meteorological observations.

Figure  2.  The rhythm of daylight and darkness.

Figure  3.  Average dates of arrival and departure of the period of lasting frost.

Figure  4.  Four expressions of winter temperatures.

Figure  5.  The advance and retreat of the snow frontier.

Figure  6.  Snow and inland ice conditions for north and south Finland.

Figure  7.  Disappearance of lake ice.

Figure  8.  Mean and maximum depths of frost penetration in various soils.

Figure  9.  Sea ice conditions around the Finnish coast.

Figure 10.  The impact of winter on the Baltic Sea.

Figure 11.  Development of the ice profile at the approaches to selected Finnish harbours.

Figure 12.  The principal types of icebreaker constructed in Hietalahti (Sandviken) yards, Helsinki.

Figure 13.  A sequence of ice situation charts for 1965: (1) January 26, 1965.

Figure 14.  A sequence of ice situation charts for 1965: (2) March 2, 1965.

Figure 15.  A sequence of ice situation charts for 1965: (3) April 6, 1965.

Figure 16.  Winter operations of the icebreaker 'Sisu' for 1963.

Figure 17.  Winter operations of the icebreaker 'Tarmo' in the winter of 1962–3.

Figure 18.  Dates of departure of last ship and of arrival of first ship at six Finnish ports during the winters from 1930–31 to 1963–4.

Figure 19.  Snowfall and snow removal in Helsinki for the winter 1961–2.

Figure 20.  Frost upheaval and the highway network.

Figure 21. Generation of electricity in Finland.

Figure 22. City lights.

Figure 23. Loggers camps in south Finland, winter 1964–5.

Figure 24. Graphs of winter heating requirements and costs.

Figure 25. Winter building conditions in Finland.

Figure 26. Monthly rhythms for selected Finnish economic activities.

Figure 27. Monthly registered unemployed for Finland's eleven employment districts in 1964.

Figure 28. Rhythms of employment for three different sectors of the Finnish economy.

Figure 29. A flow diagram of cellulose exports during the winter navigation season 1948.

Figure 30. Seasonal trading adjustments in 1963 for the inland softwood centre of Kajaani.

Figure 31. A summer frost investigaion in Karislojo, 1880.

Figure 32. Summer frost damage in Finnish marks per hectare of cultivated land, 1952.

Figure 33. A bill for winter.

# Foreword

This book is an essay upon winter and the struggle with winter conditions in the northernmost independent country in the world. As a matter of fact, Finland must contest the consequences of high latitude throughout the entire year, and a large share of its summer activities are thus aimed at helping survival through the winter. But winter is the critical period and it puts human invention and innovation to their hardest test. To describe winter and daily life in winter is therefore to enter into the core of the existence of the country. And, save for some of the picturesque sides, it is a theme which has been surprisingly neglected.

The origins of this book lie partly in the curiosity of one of its authors about the impact of ice and snow in the Scandinavian countries. In a way, it had its first expression in a short paper on 'Finland and the Winter Freeze' (*Geography*, *XXIV*, 4, 1939, 221–9). Conversations with Henrik Ramsay, whose book *I Kamp med Östersjöns Isar* was a source of inspiration for Chapter III, sustained interest at a later stage. Pierre Deffontaines's stimulating study *L'Homme et l'Hiver au Canada* nursed the idea for a parallel essay on Finland. Translation of the idea into action was due to the prompting of Henrik Antell and Hillar Kallas.

The winter theme has not been treated in its entirety. The aspects investigated have been neither pressed to their ultimate conclusions nor approached in a completely systematic and scientific manner. Although this book is designed to help the general reader towards a fuller understanding of the circumstances that surround daily life in a high latitude land, it is also hoped that it might stimulate specialists to consider in greater detail some of the issues that it discusses.

Winter has always stirred mankind. In its beginnings are bred anxieties: in its endings, hopes. Finland's overworked folk-lore includes its own apotheosis of cold. Transmitted in the oral tradition, crystallized by Elias Lönnrot and in William Kirby's translation, Wäinämöinen sings in Rune I of the national epic:

> In the cold my song was resting,
> Long remained in darkness hidden.
> I must draw my songs from coldness,
> From the frost must I withdraw them.

So many specialists from different fields of enquiry in Finland have given generously of their time and energy to make this study possible that it is impossible to acknowledge them all individually. Their particular contributions are acknowledged in the text, the maps and the graphs. Among the plates, the Finnish Foreign Ministry has kindly supplied 5, 7, 8, 9, 10, 11, 12, 13, 14, 15 and 16; the Finnish National Museum 1, 3 and 4; and the Ateneum 6. Permission to quote from F. P. Magoun Jr., *The Kalevala*, W. F. Kirby, *Kalevala*, and from Georges Duhamel, *Chant du Nord*, has been given by the Harvard University Press, J. M. Dent and Sons, and the Mercure de France respectively. The maps and diagrams have been drawn by Kenneth Wass of University College London.

W.R.M.<br>H.S.

October, 1966

# Part I  The Problem, its Causes and Effects

Winter is largely an expression of latitude. In general, the higher the latitude, the more severe and the longer the winter. Finland is a country in high latitudes. In the cycle of its seasons, winter is dominant. This dominance is the major physical fact to which Finns have to accommodate themselves. In the process they have encountered a multitude of problems. Accordingly, the study of the causes and effects of winter has been and remains a primary concern of their scientists. Legends about winter have been created, observations on it have been assembled, terms of reference for it have been devised, statistics about it have been refined. The advance and the retreat of the frontiers of ice and of snow, with their transformation of water and land, are the main effects of winter. The recurrence of these conditions is a climatic certainty and the impression that they create is powerful. O. V. Johansson, the father of Finnish meteorology, summarized the situation succinctly – 'C'est l'hiver qui donne à l'année son cachet au nord'.

# The Nature of the Problem

*Frostiana*

Ice and snow have always had a strange appeal to those who do not have to live with them. In the case of the English, they have entered the sub-conscious as picturesque features more closely associated with fiction than with fact. Comfort rather than discomfort spring first to mind, with Mr. Pickwick on the ice and Dingley Dell deep in Christmas card snow. Ice and snow have also been taken to heart nationally both as a challenge and as a relaxation – the ice and snow of other lands, that is to say. Epics in high latitudes have enabled a vicarious appreciation of them; while the vigorous promotion of winter sporting at the turn of the century by such pioneers as E. C. Richardson and Sir Arthur Lunn has led to a completely different social and economic view of winter. In 1842, the Finnish newspaper *Helsingfors Morgonblad* [1] commented with wonder upon a *glaciarium* in Baker Street, where the English might skate on artificial ice. A century later, a cargo of Norwegian snow for a Hampstead ski competition wasted away in a London dock while awaiting an import licence. *Frostiana*, the title of a book published in 1814, is a suitable word to cover the follies and foibles [2] of a people denied the pleasures associated with frost and snow.

*Frostiana* was 'printed and published on the ice on the River Thames' at the time of the last great frost fair. The intense winters which give rise to such events are associated with extensions of the continental high pressure system over the British Isles – and especially with their persistence over south-east England. Such situations provide an intermittent, bitter-sweet taste of an annual feature of the seasonal rhythm of continental northern Europe.

In few countries is the impact of the winter constituent in this rhythm more pronounced than in Finland. Because of its intensity and duration, winter insinuates itself everywhere. It is a season that has called for a variety of adjustments in day-to-day life. Men have retreated from it, mounted assault upon it and taken advantage of it.

## The Singularity of the Experience

Hard winters are experienced by other nations than Finland; but either their political frames are larger and they have more room for manoeuvre or they do not experience the same degree and duration of cold and darkness. Pierre Deffontaines [3], in his study of man and winter in Canada, has focused attention on the province of Quebec. But, the occupied parts of Quebec (and, indeed, inhabited Canada at large) are located in relatively low latitudes. Quebec is exceptional in that it lies in temperate latitudes on the east side of a continent into which sub-Arctic winter conditions trespass. Its winters are harder than those of Finland; but because of its more southerly setting, they are lighter and brighter.

Finland cannot escape the fact that it lies in higher latitudes (60° and 70° north) than any other independent country. Its fulcrum is farther north than that of Iceland. Norway could lay claim to a similar location, extending farther north than Finland, but it also stretches farther south. Parts of it, too, suffer the same degree of what Olaus Magnus called 'vehement darkness'. But Norway has a powerful maritime component in its setting. It is washed by the warm waters of the North Atlantic drift. The climate of coastal Norway has a higher positive thermal anomaly than that of any other country in the world. Winter rules on its fells, but its coastal margins experience remarkably temperate conditions. Finland's maritime background is less favourable; it looks to the brackish, virtually tideless waters of the inner Baltic Sea, which only temper its climate to a limited degree. As winter advances, a minor pole of cold establishes itself over the north-central part of the country.

In one respect, Finland experiences a circumstance unique to the lands of north-west Europe. Although it has a thousand miles of coastline, ice cuts off Finland to a greater or lesser degree from access to the sea for a substantial part of the year. None of the other countries of northern Europe experiences the same complete girdle of sea ice. Baltic Sweden knows it north of Stockholm, but Sweden has an ice-free coast to the west. Along its eastern coast Denmark witnesses a limited ice cover in harder winters. Russia has a parallel experience along its Baltic littoral, but it has a stretch of ice-free coast in the north-west Arctic as well as along its Black Sea littoral.

Finland's situation is underlined by J. L. Runeberg [4] in a manuscript fragment from an uncompleted poem:

> Vi Europas förpost mot naturen,
> Mellan isar är vår lager skuren
> Och vårt bröd vi ryckt ur is och snö

(We are Europe's outpost against the world of nature, our civilization blooms in the icy regions of the north, and our bread is snatched from out of frost and snow.)

These physical facts cause human problems. They have called and continue to call for ingenious and enterprising environmental adjustments. For the relatively small numbers of outsiders who have experienced what Arthur de Capell Brooke called this 'region of congelation', the solutions have been a source of lively curiosity. Their observations have given rise to something of a legend about Finland's winter.

## The Legend of Winter

The legend of the Finnish winter has been compiled and sustained by generations of travellers, traders and sailors from more temperate climes. From the earliest descriptions of the sixteenth century Olaus Magnus to the dramatic reports from the Winter War of 1939–40, the Finnish winter has been a source of continuous wonder and of intermittent concern to the people of Western Europe.

The image of Finland as a winter land first took shape through the widely circulated *Compendious History of the Goths, Swedes, Vandals and other Northern Nations*, published in Italy by Olaus Magnus in 1555 [5]. The history was accompanied by a fine pictorial map, the *Carta Marina*. The map was adorned with a miscellany of winter features. It showed an ice bridge between Sweden and Finland over the central Bothnian Sea. Reindeer, drawing sledges, raced over it. To the south-east, skiers with their long poles, made their way across the Finnish Gulf, while cavalry were ranged in battle array to fight 'most horribly' on its icy surface. Seals lay on ice floes in the Bothnian Gulf. Archers moved on their snow skates over the northern fells. The woodcuts that embellished F. J. Fickler's German edition of the text added vignettes of frozen waterways, a selection of shoes for horses (spiked 'with crooked irons and sharp nails') to wear on the ice and the fragile fantasies of snow crystals as they were revealed by the magnifying glass.

Olaus Magnus wrote of devices to combat ice and of efforts to employ it. Citizens of besieged forts, such as the outpost of Viborg (Viipuri), poured water upon their walls, 'the bitter cold co-operating with them' to convert the stockades into unassailable barriers of ice, that shone like 'looking-glasses'. In such a situation, soldiers fought 'more against the waters, than the weapons'. The hardy natives even used frost to protect their bodies against the cold:

'The same Finlanders use also, for to defend their bodies, partly corselets of Sea Calves skin, tanned with lime; and some use Elk skins with the hair on; and this they suffer to freeze, if they war in winter, by pouring cold water on it; nor will that Ice that sticks to the hairs without, melt by the sweating of him that carrieth it, when it is once frozen.'

Icy helmets upon their heads and woollen socks over their shoes completed their protection. Equally hardy horses bore them into their wintry battles.

The compilations of Olaus Magnus, who was an ecclesiast rather than a natural historian and an outcast from the See of Uppsala rather than a resident in the north, were complemented by the publications of the French academicians who journeyed to the Tornio valley in 1736 to determine the figure of the earth. The graphic observations on winter hardship that accompanied their astronomical investigations were sources of delight to several generations of encyclopaedists. Who could resist

Un froid si grand que la langue et les lèvres se gelôient sur le champ contre la tasse, lorsqu'on voulôit boire de l'eau-de-vie, qui était la seule liqueur qu'on put tenir assez liquide pour la boire, et ne s'en arrachôient que sanglantes?

The relished descriptions by Maupertuis [6] and Outhier [7] told of rivers turned to marble; of reindeer sleighs drawn at the speed of a bird's flight; of Lapp bonfires, which only served to melt the snow in order to transform it into a threshold of ice; of Réamur's thermometer which fell to $-37°$ ($-46°$ Celsius); of people so mutilated by cold that they were deficient of arms and legs; of the northern lights and of the low altitude of the sun which cast a man's shadow ten times as long as himself upon the flat white snow.

For the more scientifically discerning, A. F. Skjöldebrand [8] added precise details of the rigours recorded by Mr. Hellant of the Swedish Academy. On 23 January 1760 at 7.00 a.m., in Torneå, the thermometer read $-34°$ Réamur ($-42\frac{1}{2}°$ Celsius); at midnight, $-55\frac{1}{4}°$R. At Jukkasjärvi, two degrees farther north on the same day at 12.00 noon, it read $-41\frac{1}{4}°$ R. ($-51\frac{1}{2}°$ C.). In keeping with the spirit of his age, Skjöldebrand entitled his travellogue a 'picturesque journey'. His comments on 'the extreme vicissitudes of the climate' were couched in appropriate language. They produced 'a sublime contrast of beauty and horror'.

Among authors who travelled to Finland for pleasure none savoured its winter splendours and miseries more fully than Edward Clarke [9]. His 'ice pilgrimage' from Stockholm carried him across the familiar post road from Grissleham to Eckerö, through the Åland and Åbo archipelagoes to the Finnish mainland. His diaries of December 1799, and January 1800, recall the hazards of his journey, with wide detours to reach destinations tantalizingly near at hand.

Seal-hunters, with iron-shod safety pikes, preceded Clarke's party over the ice.

'The pikes used to ascertain the safety of a passenger are about six feet in length, having at the lower extremity an iron spike with a sharp and strong hook. The spike is used to try the thickness of the ice. If, after two or three stabs with this iron spike, the water do not spout up, the ice will bear a horse; and if it do not rise after a single blow, but only appears after a second stroke, it is considered as fit to support a man. The hook attached to this spike is for the purpose of dragging out the bodies of those who are unfortunate enough to slip through the crevices, or fall into the holes, which are deceitfully covered with a thin icy superficies.'

At the end of the crossing to Björkö, beyond Kumlinge, Clarke was presented with a remarkable vision of two horses statuesque upon an ice-clad rock.

'Being heated by drawing the sledges, drops of sweat had congealed into long icicles, sticking out, like bristles, all over their bodies and hanging in such long and thick stalactites from the nostrils, that it seemed dangerous to attempt to break them off, for fear of tearing away the flesh with them: all their shaggy manes and tales and hair were thus covered with a white opaque crust.'

The sleigh ride across the Turvesi passage was conducted in a temperature of 46°F. below freezing point. The lids of Clarke's left eye froze together; his 'English servant's face was frozen'; 'the interpreter's nose was turned as white as the snow itself'; their dog 'had one of its legs frozen so stiff that it stuck to his belly as if it had been glued and we could not remove it'; icicles formed upon the knees of the horses and the poor creatures tried to bite them off. There was indeed, 'reason to apprehend the freezing of the blood in one's veins'. Add to this that their madeira wine froze solidly in its bottle and that a hammer was needed to break bread that 'glittered like loaf sugar', and the behaviour of familiar things in a frosty climate was driven home.

But Åland was Finland at its most moderate and most maritime. Arthur de Capell Brooke spent December 1821 in the sub-Arctic circumstances of the Tornio valley in 'Russian Lapland'. During his two hundred mile journey, he suffered from blizzards, frost bite and boisterous reindeer. Insufficient light made frost bite difficult to detect before the face acquired 'the whiteness and almost hardness of marble'.

Winter pursued both Clarke and Brooke into their lodgings. Clarke described the scene more graphically.

'Whenever the door of our apartment was opened, the rushing in of the cold air caused a very remarkable phenomenon, by converting the warm vapour of the room into a whirling column or cloud of snow which, being instantaneous in its formation, was turned round with great rapidity.'

Brooke was more explicit about the loud cracking noises emitted by the timber houses.

'The houses are built of fir (and the noise) is occasioned by the congelation of the resinous juices of the wood, before it becomes thoroughly seasoned.'

Such curiosities partly compensated for the hazards and hardships. So did the enchantment of the winter scene. James Thomson, who contemplated it from a comfortable distance, made the descriptions of Maupertuis an apotheosis of Tornio's winter. In his narrative poem, *The Seasons*, a romantic image was published for the English-speaking world in 1746. The valley was illumined beneath

> . . . dancing meteors, that ceaseless shake
> A waving blaze refracted o'er the heavens,
> And vivid moons, and stars that keener play
> With doubled lustre from the glossy waste.

Brooke experienced it under the same streamers of the aurora and the lustre of the moon, hoar-frosted so that

'the sparkle of innumerable crystals from the surrounding illumination brought to the recollection the tales of fairy-land. It seemed almost as if we were passing through an enchanted forest, and that Nature was displaying to us her magic wonders to cheer the hours of night. With our strange figures thickly encrusted with hoar frost and rime and hurrying silently along, we had less the appearance of men than of unearthly beings, or a band of goblins, skimming the waste, to perform their midnight orgies and dance with Lapland witches.'

Bayard Taylor [10] travelled by day through the woodlands of Tornio valley, momentarily forgetting the threat of 'snowthalmia' and the cold that made him 'feel like a statue'. He described their

'silence, whiteness and wonderful variety of snowy adornment. The weeping birches leaned over the road, and formed white-fringed arches, the firs wore mantles of ermine, and ruffs and tippets of the softest swansdown. Snow, wind and frost had worked the most wonderful transformations in the forms of the forest. Here were kneeling nuns, with their arms hanging listlessly by their sides, and the white cowls falling over their faces, there lay a warrior's helmet; lace curtains, torn and ragged, hung from the points of little Gothic spires; caverns, lined with starry incrustations, silver palm leaves, doors, loopholes, arches and arcades were thrown together in fantastic confusion . . . It was an enchanted land, where you could scarcely breathe, lest a breath might break the spell.'

Georges Duhamel [11] recorded the detail of a vignette seen through a railway carriage window, as his wood-burning engine sent up its exaggerated winter plume of steam –

'Regarde, voici la campagne. Elle est toute sucrée. On dirait un grand sorbet, une vaste pièce de confisérie. Le givre du matin étincelle sur les bouleaux. Parfois, passe un souffle de brise et le givre aussitôt s'envole. Un million de petits miroirs se prênnent à tournoyer pour d'imaginaires alouettes.'

It is the scene that traditionally prevails in February – Helmikuu, in Finnish, which means, 'the month of pearls'.

Such views of winter were all very well for the dilettante or the tourist who could withdraw from it at will. Winter was different for those who had to live there all the time. Outdoor work might not only be a hardship in itself. It might also be accompanied by risks. In their daily business, for example, postal authorities suffered and continue to suffer losses of postboats and of postmen [12].

Churchmen have faced the same hazards on their pastoral visits (they, too, suffer their intermittent casualties). In Yrjö Kokko's *Way of the Four Winds* [13], one of the Lappish characters, Inkeri-Elli, succumbed to the fierce cold itself. Nor have winter's problems lost anything in the telling by mariners. Reports sent back by consular officers from Finland have graphic tales of vessels lost as a result of 'collision in the ice'. Some, such as *The Deerfoot* of Shields in December 1863, were caught in the winter freeze and 'crushed by ice'. Shipwrecked sailors were reported frozen to death and buried at Korpo in 1862. Some vessels were imprisoned in harbours and their crews had to be dispatched home by devious overland routes by consular agents. In 1859, Consul Crowe wrote encouragingly from Helsinki that the harbour authorities of Oulu had purchased a steam tug 'which would prevent vessels from being frozen in after having been loaded and cleared, as has happened to British vessels at that port as early as October' [14].

Successive British naval expeditions to the Baltic added to the legend of its treacherous winters. As the Northern Wars were drawing to an end, Admiral Norris concluded a report of 11 September 1720, by writing, 'The bad season does now come on so fast that the end of the month is the longest time we would venture to stay in these parts.' In the same context, Lord Stanhope wrote to the Swedish king of 'the backwardness of seamen to list themselves if they feared they must winter' in Sweden and Finland. The *Atlas Maritimus* probably drew its information from these same naval sources when recording that the Bothnian Sea was 'one solid rock of ice for four or five months together'. During the Crimean War, there was a similar reluctance on the part of the British and French fleets to linger in the Baltic arena as autumn approached. In late August 1854, it was reported that the French expeditionary force was anxious to destroy the fortifications of Åland's Bomarsund immediately and that 'an unwillingness to remain there in winter may somewhat influence the desire'. 'The month of September in the Baltic corresponds in severity with November here', observed a correspondent of *The Times* in 1855. The popular press exaggerated the severity of the winter. The *Illustrated London News* produced pictures of the British fleet with yard-long icicles hanging from the rigging and ice-sheathed hulls, and wrote lugubriously that 'rolling masses of half-sunken ice can for many days infest the whole Baltic'. The navy had an almost indecent fear of getting stuck in the ice and the Admiralty planned its list 'of places where ships can go in case of ice' [15].

Reports from military campaigns reinforced these impressions. Finland's skiing battalions were well known outside the north. From the sixteenth century, Klaus Fleming's name was associated with the Savo regiment, south Karelia maintained a ski regiment and Ostrobothnian skiers were renowned for their invasion of the White Sea coast. Jakob de la Gardie's forces in the early seventeenth century were believed to include 4,000 Finnish ski troops. Ice played a critical role during Finland's war of 1808–9, when Finnish and Swedish troops were able to withdraw in mid-March across the frozen Åland Sea to the Swedish mainland; while to the north, Russian troops crossed the ice bridge of the Quarken to harry

Umeå [16]. This inkling of ice, if not of the snow upon it, led to British plans for recruiting 'skating battalions' during the winter of 1854. Skiing was scarcely known to the British, but skating was familiar.

Following a nineteenth century decline in the use of the ski as a military appurtenance, it was restored to a position of eminence during Finland's most critical war – the Winter War of 1939–40. The war coincided with a hard winter and the military incidents and campaigns on the eastern front have become legendary as much for the physical conditions under which they took place as for the sake of the events themselves. Never in their history had the Finns used winter more fully in military defence and attack – turning ice and snow to their peculiar advantage and melting into their countryside in white camouflage. The war was witnessed by more foreign observers than all of Finland's other military engagements put together [17]. They came (like James Byron) through the frozen sea from Stockholm in ships 'quivering with the travail of their screws' [18] and gasping for steam as they fought the ice; they met a magpie land, black-and-white save when the sun shone, the home of the Snow Queen. Again the legend of winter was enlarged.

## The Record of the Facts

Since Finns first occupied their land, they have passed on by oral tradition their observations upon the cycle of the seasons. The earliest encouragement to keep regular records for scientific purposes dates from the earlier eighteenth century. It sprang out of the curiosity of natural philosophers such as the Uppsala astronomer Andreas Celsius and the medical botanist Carl Linnaeus. Celsius published his own observations in the Proceedings of the Swedish Academy of Sciences in 1740. Carl Linnaeus, writing in *Lärda Tidningar* in 1749, exhorted readers to make observations on nature, which might be built up into the so-called *Calendaria florae et faunae*. A good many parish priests already began to make phenological records in their church books before mid-eighteenth century legislation provided them with a special responsibility in the columns of the census forms. Church archives are consequently a useful source from which to piece together the detail of earlier climatic conditions.

The first significant climatic record of facts in Finland was made by Johan Lecke in Åbo between 1748–63. Among other items with which he concerned himself were the maximum and mimimum temperatures, wind directions and ice break-up. The lowest temperatures he recorded were −36°C. on 25 December 1750, and 7 January 1760. His formula was also followed for a number of other years between 1764–1800. In the countryside, independent observations were made in Oulu (1776–87), Sodankylä (1789) and Utsjoki (1795–7). Initiative was then taken up by the Finnish Economic Society, which circulated to its members a promemoria on meteorological observations. From country members, it also sought to stimulate an interest in recording items of farming consequence. Winter observations were to include the number of days that the soil was frozen and that sledges were used instead of wheel vehicles; the depth of frost in the soil, the depth of snow in forests and in open countryside, the date of the ice break-up and the record of summer frosts.

But it was not until the 1820's that attempts were made to produce a more systematic review of climatic conditions. Collection was initiated by Carl Christian Böcker and G. C. Hällström. Even a casual perusal of the Böcker papers in the Finnish Economic Society reflects the insistence with which he urged his friends up and down the country to make regular weather recordings [19]. At one time, there were as many as forty 'stations' in operation, the thermometers and barometers of which were supplied principally by the Society.

Böcker never lived to see the fulfilment of his work, though Finland established a 'magnetic-meteorological' observatory in Helsinki in 1844. Among its earlier endeavours was a scheme for obtaining a synoptic view of Finland's principal phenological features. The scheme derived some inspiration from the meeting of

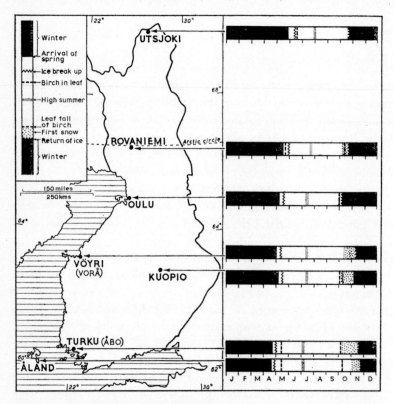

**Figure 1. Meteorological Observations**

A selection of some of the 200 meteorological and phenological observations for seven Finnish stations assembled by A. Moberg for the period 1750–1850. They are based upon twenty observations in each locality. The data are not quite complete for all of the stations illustrated.

the British Association for the Advancement of Science in 1841, where an attempt was made to initiate observations on the migrations of birds and the occurrence of flowering times throughout Europe. The programme of observations also included for the first time plans for an elementary record of the behaviour of sea ice. Figure 1 provides a selection of data for seven stations for which long term records had been kept [20].

The network of recording stations for phenological and climatological data was gradually extended and the total Finnish picture was given more precise form; but little was published until the 1880's. The first records to give a moderately satisfactory picture of Finland's winter climate were the meteorological observations for 1873–9, published by the Finnish Society of Sciences in 1880–3.

Since then, the refinement of facts about winter has taken place at a number of levels for a number of different purposes. In no area of enquiry has weather reporting been more important than in that of winter circumstances. On land, the accumulated experiences of the likely incidence of snowfall and of the establishment of critical temperatures affect a whole range of human adjustments. At sea, they are of even greater consequence, for the entire winter shipping programme is dependent on a regular and detailed knowledge of weather conditions. A scheme for a scientific record of the facts of winter sea icing was being urged by the Finnish Geographical Society in 1888–9 and a pioneer work on the ice situation outside Hangö was set in motion in 1893 [21]. Recording was in the first place the responsibility of lighthouse keepers. A special form was issued to them for observations on the thickness of ice (divided according to the various types of ice), the distribution of drift ice, pressured ice, sea lanes and open water, and the edge of the fast ice. They made returns twice a week, from which ice situation maps were compiled.

Effective ice reporting demanded speedy communication of information. Consular agents had employed the electric telegraph for transmitting knowledge of ice conditions in the Baltic to Britain and France at the time of the Crimean War. By 1860, means were available for transmitting information from Torneå to Elsinore. With his customary vision, the Finnish historian Zachris Topelius had sensed the combined significance of telegraph and steamship. In a university lecture given in 1867 [22], he declared with poetic licence, 'they are melting the ice of the Baltic and casting the north into the arms of the south'. The telegraph enabled the preparation of synoptic charts. By 1896, the assembly of information was vested in a nautical-meteorological bureau.

Finnish facts and figures, however, were not enough. International collaboration and exchange of information was needed for effective interpretation. In 1898, exchange of information on ice conditions was initiated between the Scandinavian countries and Finland, while the following year log entries were reported by ships arriving at Finnish ports. In 1902, as many as 57 ice maps were made available by ships. Through the Marine Research Institute, established in 1918, the study of the behaviour of the sea was added to that of the air. But, by then, the radio telegraph had come into operation, so that a new means of collecting and disseminating information was available. The record of facts was also demonstrated to be of more than academic interest. In the 1930's, Risto Jurva produced a formula in the shape of a cartogram to facilitate the forecasting of developments in Baltic sea ice. The formula employed the full range of past experiences as a means of forecasting future situations [23].

## The Language of Winter

In order to express the facts of winter, a considerable winter vocabulary has evolved. It is a vocabulary largely unique to place, because many of the phenomena which have given rise to it are restricted in distribution to Finland. In Finland, most of the winter features which have called forth words have been expressed in its two official languages – Finnish and Swedish. In most cases, there is no precise English equivalent. The words are not found in English because the feature is not encountered in Britain.

Winter itself falls into three distinct seasons – autumn winter (F. *syystalvi*; Sw. *höstvinter*), November and December; high winter (F. *sydäntalvi* or *keskitalvi*; Sw. *högvinter* or *midvinter*), January and February; and spring winter (F. *kevättalvi*; Sw. *vårvinter*), March and April. Intense winter frost is expressed in the Finnish word *pakkanen* (indicating a sub-zero temperature). Excessively hard winters have devastating frosts (F. *pakkastuhot*), with correspondingly disastrous consequences for cultivated trees, shrubs and plants: winters with heavy snow also cause tree damage (F. *lumituho*). Associated with the depths of winter are the varied snow-drift forms (F. *hankikinos*). The hardened surface or crust of the snow is *hanki* (Sw. *skare*) and when it is hard enough to bear a man it is described *hanki kantaa miehen* (Sw. *skarföre*). In north Finland the conifers may be embossed to the extent of thousands of kilogrammes per tree with frozen snow (F. *tykky*). Along the coast and lakeshore, sheaths of ice develop over and around boulders (F. *porehia, poreilla*).

Movement around in such a land has hitherto been on the runner (F. *jalas*; Sw. *mede*) and the condition of going is described in the Finnish word element *keli* (Sw. *före*). The condition of winter going, originally by sleigh, but by transfer to all conditions of going, is *talvikeli* (Sw. *vinterföre, slädföre*). Sometimes, lakes and bays freeze without a snow cover and the going over such a surface is *kierakeli* (Sw. *isföre*). The winter routeways that take to frozen water or swamp are *talvitiet* (Sw. *vintervägar*). Winter log roads (F. *tukkitiet*) are opened up into the forest depths. Both are seasonally signposted.

For sea ice, there is a special terminology. The first suspicion of ice which appears on the surface of the water – film-like in thickness, but elastic in texture – bears the name *jääkalvo* (Sw. *ishinna*). Its millimetres are soon converted into centimetres and become *jääkuori* (Sw. *isskorpa*), perhaps best interpreted as ice rind. The young winter ice into which this rind develops is called *sinijää* (Sw.

*blåis*). It is frequently opaque and opacity calls for a special expression – *teräsjää* (Sw. *kärnis*).

*Avanto* (F.) – *vak* (Sw.) is the hole hewn with the *jäätuuri* (Sw. *isbill*) through the ice – to let down fish nets or fish lines, to haul up domestic water, even to provide an opening for a cold dip after a *sauna*. And from the same lake surface, blocks of ice are sawn to store under a sawdust cover in the ice pit or ice cellar against the heat of the summer.

*Pälvät* (F.) – *barmark* (Sw.) – or thaw holes, which begin to gape in the snow around tree trunks and boulders, are the first sign of the growing power of the sun at the end of winter. *Kohva* (F.), a mixture of slush and water by day which freezes into new ice layers by night, forms above the solid ice. *Jäänlähtö* (Sw. *islossning*), the break up of the ice, results in ice jams on the water courses and the invasion of their valleys by flood ice and thaw water (F. *uhkujää*).

For several weeks before the summer sun dries up the spring slush and converts frozen waterways into open fairways, there is a season of difficulty when the going is bad (F. *kelirikko*; Sw. *menföre*). It is a perilous season for country communications, especially on the *jäätie* or ice road across the water. According to the Kuopio way of expressing it, a *puoli suksin, puoli venehin* (half-ski, half-boat) situation develops. What, in the skier's terminology, are good conditions (F. *luistava keli*) degenerate into watery conditions (F. *vesikeli*). The situation is at its worst when warm sunny days begin to alternate with sharp frosty nights. The same weather conditions are responsible for 'heaving' autumn sown grain out of the ground (F. *routia*; Sw. *tjälskott*).

Ice terminology has its local expressions. In his book *Färdmän från isarna*, Jan Sundfeldt [24] illustrates the winter terminology of the inhabitants from Vasa skerries. *Stamp* is the belt of broken ice, difficult to negotiate, which lies beyond the firm rim of the mainland ice. *Randbruten* is the term used to describe the clutter of ice slabs thrown up on an extended front by winter storms. *Vred* is the long embankment which the wind builds up from broken ice against the mainland ice. *Kall* is the fragmented ice on the shore cut off by the movement of sea waters and is a place name element that is fairly common in coastal districts.

It is natural that the terminology of winter should have rich dialect variations. The University Research Institute, *Castrenianum*, which is the keeper of a great wealth of dialect materials, has card indices from which the language of winter can be appreciated in its regional context [25].

## Finland and the Winter Freeze

'Finland is a country whose history has been entirely dominated by one geographical fact – its extremely severe climate', wrote a nineteenth century British author. It was a conclusion in keeping with the fashionable determinist philosophies of the time as propagated by Ratzel and Buckle. It gave a new twist to the impact made by Finland's winter on the outer world. The impact sprang from description

– and description which was deficient of the rich winter vocabulary that had developed in the vernacular. With the aid of scientific instruments, Finland was gradually able to give a new precision to the facts of its winters. The fuller the facts and the longer the record of them, the greater the understanding brought to bear upon the problems of winter. The next chapter will look at the facts as they throw light on the causes of the problem and the associated physical consequences.

BIBLIOGRAPHY

[1] Helsingfors, 1842, 25, 4.

[2] Its full title is *Frostiana, A History of the River Thames in a Frozen State*, London, 1814.

[3] P. Deffontaines, *L'Homme et l'Hiver au Canada*, Paris, 1957.

[4] Manuscript in *Borgå Samlingen*.

[5] In the original *Historia de Gentibus septentrionalibus;* English edition, London, 1658.

[6] P. L. M. de Maupertuis, *La Figure de la Terre*, Paris, 1738.

[7] R. Outhier, *Journal d'un Voyage fait au Nord en 1736-37*, Paris, 1744.

[8] A. F. Skjöldebrand, *A picturesque Journey to the North Cape*, London, 1813.

[9] E. Clarke, *Travels in various Countries of Europe*, London, 1824.

[10] B. Taylor, *Northern Travel*, London, 1858, p. 66.

[11] *Chant du Nord*, Paris, 1929, p. 79.

[12] L. W. Fagerlund, Anteckningar rörande samfärdseln emellan Sverige och Finland över Ålands Haf, *Åland*, VIII, Helsingfors, 1925, includes many accounts of winter hazards.

[13] London, 1954.

[14] W. R. Mead, The Birth of the British Consular System in Finland, *The Norseman*, XIV, 2, 1957.

[15] W. R. Mead, Finland and the Landfall of British Authority, *The Norseman*, XVI, 1, 1958.

[16] *Sveriges krig 1808 och 1809, Generalstabens krigshistoriska Afdelning*, Stockholm, 8, 1921.

[17] J. Langdon-Davies, *Finland, the first total War*, London, 1940.

[18] (James Bramwell) *The Unfinished Man*, London, 1957.

[19] Correspondence in the archive of Finska Hushållningssällskapet, Åbo.

[20] A. Moberg, *Om de ifrån år 1750 till år 1850 i Finland gjorda natural-historiska Daganteckningar och deras Betydelse i Klimatologiskt Hänseende*, Helsingfors, 1857.

[21] *Fennia*, 12, 1, Sällskapets för Finlands Geografi Förhandlingar, 19, Jan., 1895, g.2.

[22] *Föreläsningar*, mss. University Library, Helsinki.

[23] R. Jurva, Die Eisverhältnisse an den Küsten Finnlands, *Fennia*, 1937, 64, 1.

[24] J. Sundfeldt and T. Johnson, *Färdmän från isarna*, Helsingfors, 1964.

[25] Dr. Pentti Virtaranta has kindly provided the two following illustrations. The words are not precise synonyms, but appertain to the general condition described. (*a*) Towards spring, water often appears on the surface of the ice, is itself frozen and gives rise to a twofold cover of ice. Such ice coverings may be called: *kerrosjää, kerta, kertajää, kohma, kohmajää, kohmanne, kohmo, kohmojää, kohojää, kohva, kohvajää, komo, komojää, komse, komisko, kopanne, komsujää, korppa, krohmojää, krohojää, kropojää, kynsikatko, pono, ponojää, porejää, roukko, uhkujää.* (*b*) The following words mean 'a hard, transparent ice': *hydelmä, jää(n)riitta, kaljama, kierä jää, kire, kirkas jää, kirsi, kissinnahka, kohkojää, kohma (jää), krohelojää, krohjää, lasijää, nilppu, rahe, rahenuottajää, rahijää, rahkajää, rahke, raudasjää, raudus, raudusjää, rautajää, riitte, riitta, routajää, syksyjää, terasjää, kohva, kohvajää, korejää, krahu.*

'For the north, winter is the only real season of the year. Spring is but a promise, although it makes an impressive beginning; summer is an illusion, though because of a few warm days or at most weeks, people believe it to be true; autumn is a a dying, spring's promise and summer's illusion cast into a dark grave. But winter is indeed of our essence: snow, ice and cold are a part of our nature. Winter never betrays us. Its arrival is a certainty.'

Such was the opinion expressed by Toivo Pekkanen, a late member of the Finnish Academy, in his novel *Nuorin veli* ('The Youngest Brother'). But if the arrival of winter is assured by the mechanics of celestial circumstance, the character of winter is highly variable. In considering the physical causes and effects of winter, it is proposed to begin with the consequences of latitude, which determine the supply of heat energy received from the sun as well as the rhythm of daylight and darkness. Latitude is modified by land and water distributions as well as by major atmospheric air movements. Over the face of the country winter expresses itself visually in ice and snow. It transforms the appearance of the land. The advance and retreat of the frost frontier and the advance and retreat of the snow frontier are the realities from which human experiences are derived [1]. The advance of the frost and snow frontiers affect the sea that surrounds Finland as significantly as they affect the land. The reactions of the sea are a different story. But, first, winter must be defined.

## A Definition of Winter

Winter was defined popularly before it was defined scientifically. The significance of popular definitions was underlined by an early nineteenth century writer, Samuel Ödman. 'Country sayings about the weather and prophecies I seek out assiduously,' he wrote, 'for sometimes they are like the smoke which reveals a hidden spark and I see them as an economic cabbala which is transmitted *per traditionem oralem*' [2]. Few countries have assembled their weather lore with such diligence as Finland [3].

Country lore ascribes the beginning of winter to 14 October. Winter is ushered in by the week of Pirkko (Sancta Birgitta), a saint whose name day is 7 October. Its onset is anticipated by the use of the Finnish word *talviyöt* (winter nights) for 13–15 October. October is followed by *Marraskuu* (November), literally the month of lifelessness. High winter (F. *sydäntalvi*) is reached in February and the midpoint of winter (F. *talvenselkä, talvennapa*) is generally accepted as 15 February. In some old calendars, it was regarded as coincident with St. Paul's Day (26 January). In the parish of Sääminki, for example, it is said that St. Paul's day is 'the navel of winter' (*Paaveli on talven napa*); in Pielavesi, St. Paul's Day is 'half way through winter' (*Paavali on puoli talvea*).

Shrove Tuesday was commonly looked upon as the beginning of lighter days; though it generally anticipated winter's climax. Carl Linnaeus described the period 20–22 February as the 'iron days' of winter. St. Matthew's Day (24 February) has a wide reputation as the time when 'the gates of the snow are opened' (*Matista lumiportit auki*, in the parish of Kangasala). More picturesquely, it is said that 'Matthew opens the snowgates and puts a white cap nine times on the head of the tree stumps' (*Matti avaa lumiportit ja lyö yhdeksän lakkia kannon päähän*).

Balancing 14 October in the country calendar of the winter season is 14 April, the day that marks the beginning of the summer half of the year. The nights of 12–14 April have been described as *suviyöt*, perhaps deriving from the older east and north Finnish name for April, *Sulamakuu* or *Suvikuu* (possibly the month of thaw).

The simplest scientific definition has a thermal basis – the period when the daily mean temperature remains below freezing point (0°C.; 32°F.). Various attempts have been made to classify the types of winter experienced within this frame. The Dutch meteorologist C. Easton has approached the problem chronologically and has divided the winters of western Europe into nine categories [4]. They began with 'very severe' (*grand hiver*) and proceeded through 'severely cold'; 'normal, but rather cold'; 'normal'; 'normal, but rather mild'; 'mild'; 'warm' and 'very warm'.

Joachim Blüthgen has used a chorographical approach [5]. He has tabulated and mapped the various winter regimes experienced in Finland. The regimes are a synthesis of the duration and nature of frost and of snow conditions, of insolation and of the degree of variability in weather conditions. He has identified regimes that are typical for Lapland, interior Finland, Bothnian Finland, the Finnish Gulf coastlines and the Åland Islands.

In the meantime, the more mathematically inclined meteorologists have been analysing patterns of temperature behaviour within the winter period. H. Simojoki, for example, has identified nine major temperature oscillations in the winter season [6]. The probability of their recurrence is critical for forecasting.

While winter differs from place to place, and from year to year, it has also a different meaning from one group of people to another. For the migrant Lapp, though its external signs may still be lasting, winter is over when reindeer herds make for the calving grounds. The sportsman's winter conforms neither to that of the meteorologist nor to that of the phenologist. Again, public services have their own ideas about the duration of winter. Winter and summer timetables have existed since the beginning of organized transport. They have also had their different seasonal charges. Thus, the first tolls for the ferry between Eckerö and Wäddö were 10 mk. in wintertime, from St. Martin's Day (11 November) until Easter; 8 mk. from Easter until the sea was free of drift ice; 6 mk. in summertime until Michaelmas (c. 1 October) and then 8 mk. A toll from 1760 defined the winter period as 1 November–30 April; another, in 1803, as 14 October–14 April.

## A Question of Latitude

The character of Finland's winter is very much a question of latitude. It is caused primarily by a declining intake of heat energy from the sun. The diminution of insolation is a result of the oblique position of the rotating earth in relation to its plane of revolution round the sun. This condition means that the northern hemisphere is turned away from the sun from 23 September until 21 March, and that it lies in shadow for more than twelve out of 24 hours. In other words, night is longer than day. The period of shadow increases from 23 September to the winter solstice on 22 December. At the same time, the height to which the sun rises above the horizon decreases daily until its lowest position at the winter solstice is achieved. A direct consequence is that the sun's rays are projected from an increasingly low angle and correspondingly weaker in their effect. The intensity of insolation accordingly diminishes as well as the duration of insolation. After 21 December, daylight slowly lengthens until at the vernal equinox on 21 March, day and night are equal. In some parts of Finland, as in Scandinavia at large, the turn of the sun was probably celebrated with fires and with offerings to the gods – the *midvinterblot*.

The diminution in insolation received from the sun does not depend on the distance of the earth from the sun. As a matter of fact, the earth's position is closest to the sun when winter conditions prevail in the northern hemisphere. A happy consequence of this is that the period of the midnight sun in Finland north of the Arctic Circle is longer than the complementary period of complete winter darkness when the shorter distance from the earth to the sun makes for higher speed in the progression of the planet through the firmament.

The height of the sun above the horizon and the length of the day vary appreciably through Finland's ten degrees of latitude. In Helsinki, the height of the sun at noon at the equinoxes is 30°; but it is only 6½° at the winter solstice. In Oulu, the sun rises to a maximum height of 25° at the equinoxes; but only to 1·5° on 21 December. In Rovaniemi, the height of the sun's arc at the equinoxes is 23½°, while at the winter solstice, it just touches but does not rise above the horizon. The situation is illustrated in Figure 2. To the north of the latitude of Rovaniemi,

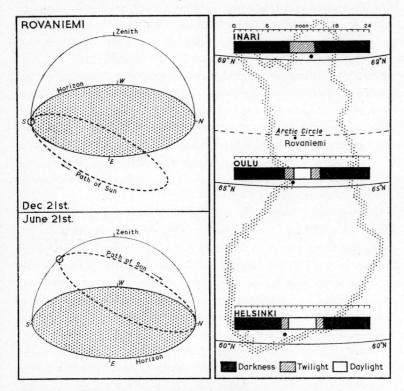

**Figure 2. The Rhythm of Daylight and Darkness**

Daylight and darkness conditions at the midwinter solstice for three selected Finnish stations, together with the midwinter and midsummer positions of the sun for Rovaniemi.

which is about a third of Finland's total length, the arc of the sun lies below the horizon for a shorter or longer period. At Utsjoki, the sun is not seen during a period of 51 days; in Ivalo, the tourist centre on the south side of Lake Inari, during one of 37 days.

But although the sun falls below the horizon, its rays are reflected into the atmosphere so that a period of dawn merging with a period of dusk gives a measure of luminosity to high latitude Finland in midwinter. Figure 2 illustrates the duration of daylight, darkness and twilight for Utsjoki, Oulu and Helsinki. Thus, the polar night at Utsjoki, even at its darkest on 21 December, is broken by four hours of twilight. The time when the sun is not seen, but when day is replaced by twilight is called *Kaamosaika*. In Oulu, at the winter solstice, 3½ hour of full daylight are prolonged by close to 3 hours of dawn or twilight; while at the equinoxes, both dawn and dusk are of a full hour's duration. If the sky is clear on the day of the winter solstice, Helsinki can have about $5\frac{1}{2}$ hours of sunshine, while morning and evening light reflected from below the horizon can add two hours of twilight. Thus, in Finland, the higher the latitude, the longer the dawn and the dusk, both absolutely and relatively. During winter, people in northern Finland are as accustomed to working in twilight as in direct sunshine. Artificial light is important for out-of-door as well as indoor work. Forest workers, for example, begin their working day with lamps, torches and floodlights.

If the winter climate of Finland were determined exclusively by latitude and its associated effect on the rays of the sun, every winter would be similar, with the least insolation and the most intense cold occurring at the midwinter solstice. Under such circumstances, the decline in temperature, the first frosts, the first snowfall and the first thaw would all be predictable and succeed each other on regular dates. In reality, the coldest month is neither December nor January, but February; while the events of the approaching as well as those of the retreating winter are highly variable from year to year.

The causes of these deviations from the solar climate are to be sought in the influence of the Baltic Sea and in the broader and deeper effects exerted on the whole of north-western Europe by the Atlantic Ocean. Because Finland lies in the track of a predominantly westerly air stream, it experiences more or less regular influxes of warm maritime air. This is especially true in the first third of the winter. The maritime air is brought in by cyclones, the passage of which usually lasts three or four days, or even longer. Their frequency in the earlier part of the winter is a primary reason why the lowest winter temperatures are generally delayed until February. Between the cyclones, cold polar air intrudes. This is associated with anti-cyclonic conditions. It yields clear sunny skies which are in great contrast to the moist, cloudy conditions associated with the passage of the cyclones. In Finnish, the south-east wind is called *vesietelä*, or the rainy southern, while the north-west wind is named *taivaan luuta* or the broom of the sky. The alternation of cyclonic and anti-cyclonic weather conditions is expressed in many proverbs, for example, the Mäntsälä saying *pakkanen pyryn perästä paha ilma pakkasesta* (frost follows the gale; stormy weather, the frost).

It is mainly due to maritime and cyclonic influences that Finnish winter is much warmer than those of most areas lying in similar latitudes. Helsinki, at latitude approximately 60°N, has a January mean temperature of $-5\cdot4$°C.; Kuopio, at 63°N, $-9\cdot3$°C.; Rovaniemi, at the Arctic Circle, $-11\cdot4$°C. The more favoured situation of Finland is clear by comparing these figures with those for corresponding latitudes in western North America. Fort Smith (60°N) has a January mean temperature of $-26\cdot2$°C.; Dawson City (c. 64°N), $-30\cdot2$°C.; Fort Yukon ($66\frac{1}{2}$°N); $-30\cdot2$°C. It has been calculated that Finland at large has a January mean temperature which is $11°$ warmer than that of the general latitude belt between 60° and 70°N.

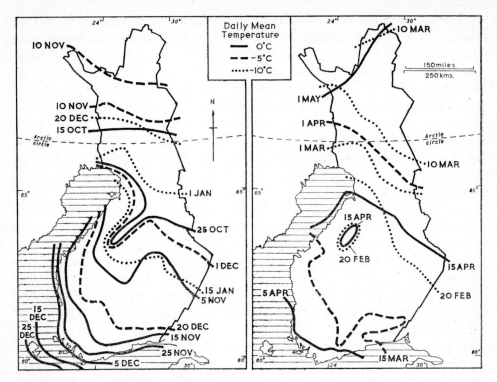

**Figure 3. Average Dates of Arrival (left) and of Departure (right) of the Period of Lasting Frost.**

The figures are for the period 1931–60 and indicate three critical daily mean temperatures. The 'cold island' of Suomenselkä, with its early arrival and delayed departure of winter, is especially noticeable. It is higher in altitude and has a lower area of surface water than most parts of Finland.

The frequency and size of cyclones experienced by Finland varies greatly from year to year. In some winters, stable continental air is maintained for long periods in the atmosphere above Finland. This results in Siberian-type winters – dry and sunny with severe frosts. In other winters, the procession of cyclones will continue almost uninterruptedly and result in an Atlantic type winter – with greater cloud cover and heavier snowfall, sleet or rain. Coastal Finland, under such circumstances, may even lack a permanent snow cover.

Normally, however, a variable period of frosts and thaws precedes the time of lasting frosts, the true winter. In average years (Figure 3, left), the period of lasting frosts, when the mean daily temperature sinks below 0°C., begins in northernmost Finland in mid-October. At Sodankylä, close to the Arctic watershed, it is about 8 October; at Utsjoki on Tana River, 10; Ivalo, 15; Rovaniemi, 18. In central Finland, as far south as the Salpausselkä, the period of lasting frosts begins in the first half of November (Pielisjärvi, 1 November; Lahti, 12 November). Along the coastlands of the Finnish gulf, lasting frosts are delayed until as late as 14 December in Mariehamn and 26 December at Utö.

The period of lasting frosts draws to an end, from region to region, at very variable times (Figure 3, right). In the south-west, it is usually April before mean daily temperatures rise above 0°C. The average dates are 1 April for Mariehamn and 6 April for Helsinki airfield. In central Finland, the period of lasting frost ends about mid-April; but it may be delayed until May in northern Finland – the average date is May 1 for Utsjoki and 8 May for Kilpisjärvi in the extreme north-west.

The invasion of winter is held back by several influential factors. First, there are the Atlantic cyclones which have already been mentioned and which give rise to a thick cloud cover. The cloud cover reduces loss of heat from the earth's surface. Secondly, development of low temperatures is delayed by the heat stored in the Baltic Sea and its gulfs. Thirdly, the heat stored in the Finnish lakes is a source of warmth until their surfaces are covered by ice. The very transformation of water into ice releases vast quantities of heat. It has been computed that the intrusion of winter upon autumn is postponed by about one week because of heat released during the autumn freeze of the lakes of Finland. The retreat of winter is correspondingly slow since the process of thaw consumes as much heat as the freeze releases. Heat needed to dissolve lake ice alone probably delays the arrival of spring by a week.

Figure 4 (A) shows the average length of the period of lasting frost. In the northernmost part of the country it is about 200 days (Kilpisjärvi has, in fact, 207 days). In central Finland, the period is reduced to 150 days (Jyväskylä and Joensuu have 148). Helsinki airport has 136 days; the south-western archipelago, from 100–110 days.

Two other criteria help to give some indication of the relative severity of winter in different parts of the country – the period of strong frost (below −5°C.) and the period of severe frost (below −10°C.). These facts are shown on Figure 4 (right). Such extreme conditions are rarely experienced in the outer archipelago. If such a phenomenon as a 'normal' winter can be conceived, daily means of −5°C. are not encountered before Christmas west of Kotka and Hamina (on the Finnish Gulf) and Kokkola (on the Bothnian Gulf). In Hangö, strong frost is not regularly registered until 18 January and lasts only until mid-March. The maritime effect is speedily dissipated inland and the period of strong frost forms the

**Figure 4. Four Expressions of Winter Temperature**

All four maps are based upon figures for the period 1931–60.

A. *Duration of Period with Daily Mean Temperatures below 0°C.*

B. *Duration of Period with Daily Mean Temperatures below −5°C and below −10°C.*

C. The map identifies four areas (a) the south-west, where the number of days with daily means from 0°C to −15°C exceeds the number of days with daily means below −5°C (b) the centre, where daily means between −5°C and −10°C are dominant (c) the north, where the period with daily means below −10°C is longer than the period with daily means between −5°C and −10°C (d) the extreme north, where the daily means between −5°C and −10°C are dominant.

D. *Means of Absolute Minimum Temperature for January.*

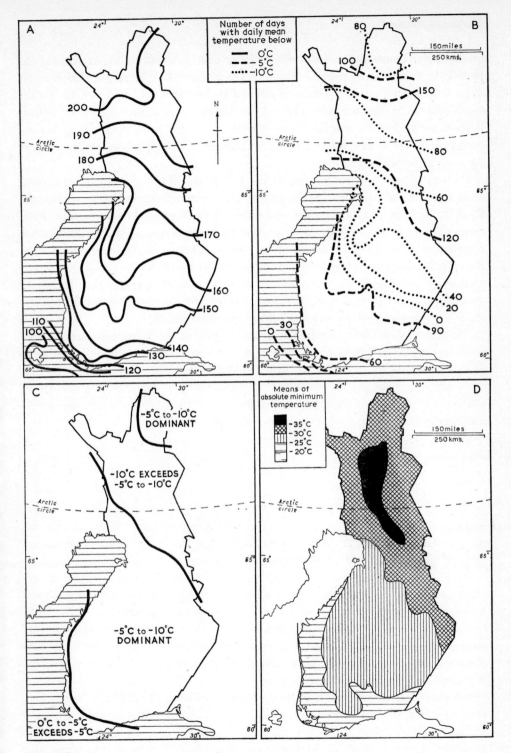

**Figure 4**

predominant component of the temperature chart. As far to the south-west as Jyväskylä, strong frost prevails from 17 December to 15 March, a period of 88 days in comparison with 70 days of mild frosts between 0°C. and −5°C. To the south-east, Ilomantsi balances 112 days of strong frost against 54 of mild frost. Rovaniemi airfield experiences strong frost from 20 November to 29 March, giving 129 days as against 56 days of mild frost. For Kilpisjärvi, the figures are 159 and 48 respectively.

Periods of severe frost belong to the north-east. They do not affect coastal areas south of the latitude of Oulu under normal circumstances. In the south-east, Punkaharju averages thirteen days of severe frost from 25 January until 7 February. The period is prolonged to 43 days in Joensuu and 49 in Nurmes. In the northern third of Finland, severe frosts are an essential characteristic of winter. Rovaniemi normally expects the daily mean to fall below −10°C. about 22 December and for this to last until about 5 March. This means that for about two-fifths of its winter period, Rovaniemi experiences severe frost. In Kilpisjärvi the figure rises to 93 days – almost half of the winter.

Fluctuations of winter conditions on either side of the dates mentioned can be considerable. A deviation from the normal of a month or more is not unusual. Positive thermal fluctuations are likely to have the most pronounced effect in the south-west; negative fluctuations, to influence most strongly the conditions in the south-east. Negative fluctuations, associated with extensions of continental high pressure, give rise to frost conditions below −20°C. – even lower than −30°C. (see Figure 4). Temperatures of −20°C. may already be experienced along the coast, but they are unlikely in the archipelagoes. The mean of absolute minimum temperature during the period 1931–60 was −20·3°C. for Helsinki; −24·2°C., for Turku and −22·9°C., for Kotka. Extremely severe frosts, below −30°C., are regular features of the climate only in the extreme east of the country and in the north. Tohmajärvi is a south-eastern station with a mean of absolute mimimum of −32·2°C. Corresponding figures for Rovaniemi and Sodankylä are −35·4°C. and −36·3°C. respectively.

Very severe frosts of −15°C. to −20°C. are a common Finnish winter experience; but lasting frosts of such severity do not occur regularly each winter. For example, in the winters of 1924–5, 1929–30 and 1934–5, no daily means below −15°C. were registered; whereas, in the two war winters of 1939–40 and 1941–2, successions of ten days with daily means below −15°C. were frequent and the absolute temperature on occasions fell close to −40°C. in south Finland and close to −50°C. in north Finland.

Siberian type winters, such as those of 1939–40, 1941–2, and 1965–6 in which such low temperatures occur, have disastrous effects upon the world of nature and man alike. In the former, for example, temperate zone vegetation may suffer seriously. Fodder plants and garden shrubs (even if wrapped in protective covering) may be destroyed. Orchards suffer particularly badly – especially trees that are not of sturdier native stock. In the 'war winters' of 1939–40 and 1941–2 half of Finland's total number of apple trees were killed; in the winter of 1955–6, a full fifth [8]. Siberian type winters, such as 1965–6, interfere with the effective operation of motor vehicles and may render railway lines so 'brittle' that they are hazardous for fast traffic.

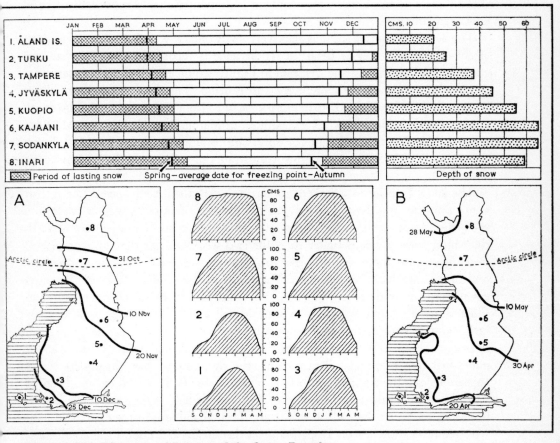

**Figure 5. The Advance and Retreat of the Snow Frontier**
Map A shows the advance of the snow frontier: Map B, its retreat. The eight snow profiles are those of the eight stations indicated by name on the graphs and identified on the map.
The profiles indicate the volume of snowfall.

## The Advance and Retreat of the Snow Frontier

Low winter temperatures automatically affect water relationships. Rain becomes snow: water, ice. Low temperatures govern the advance and retreat of the snow cover. They are the cause of the sheath of ice which envelopes lake, river and surrounding sea.

Finland has a relatively low precipitation – regionally from under 400 to 700 mm. p.a. It is wetter in the south than in the north; but the proportion of snowfall is greater in the north (50%–60%) than in the south (30%–40%). By comparison with the great eiderdown of snow that virtually smothers Norway, Finland's

37

blanket is usually light. The first snow already falls in the Lapland fells in late September. As Figure 5 shows, most of Finland north of the Arctic Circle is snow-covered by the end of October. The snow frontier advances from the north-east to cover fully half of the surface area of the country by mid-November; though the extreme south-west mainland and archipelagoes are normally free of snow at Christmas.

The accumulation of snow is relatively swift once low temperature conditions establish themselves. The detail of its advance is recorded at no less than 426 stations. The top right-hand diagram in Figure 5 indicates the average maximum depth of snow for eight different areas in Finland. The depth varies from about 20 cms. in the Åland Islands to over 70 cms. in Kajaani and Sodankylä. The depth is very variable, but it reaches a maximum in March. The Meteorological Office takes 15 March as the peak date for observations. The profiles of snowfall shown for the same eight stations in Figure 5 illustrate the situation in a winter of heavy snowfall.

The snow frontier usually retreats more swiftly than it advances. The retreat is not uniform, but depends partly on the amount of snow as well as where the snow lies. Snow in the forest melts more slowly than snow in open country. In the south, snow remains under trees for two weeks longer than in open places; in the north, for three weeks longer [9]. The snow depths in field and forest are returned for 52 recording stations. Variations in the disappearance of the snow cover are of considerable importance for wild life. Birds which over-winter in Finland are especially sensitive to snow depth and to the detail of local snow melt, both of which affect feeding possibilities.

Under average conditions, the south-west coastlands will be free of snow about mid-April (see Figure 5). By this time, the snow cover may already have dis-appeared along the coast as far north as Vaasa on the Gulf of Bothnia and Hamina on the Gulf of Finland. By the end of April about half of the face of the land is free from snow. At the end of May, only the Lapland arm in the extreme north-west retains a snow cover. Depending on the season and upon local conditions, the snow cover lasts from 100–140 days in the south and from 180–210 days in the higher parts of north Finland. Because of the relatively swift snow melt there is usually a rapid run-off and considerable evaporation.

Snowfall is a variable phenomenon temporally as well as regionally. This is illustrated by Figure 6, which shows the graphs of snowfall for the winter of 1963–4 side by side with the average monthly conditions for the years 1911–60. It is safe to say that northern Finland will experience higher snowfall than southern Finland. A complicating fact in the south-west quarter of the country is the inter-mittent intrusion of Atlantic air which may cause snow melt at any time of the winter. Snowstorms are liable to occur in south Finland until the end of April and in central Finland until mid-May.

Snow is neither a simple nor a single phenomenon. Finnish meteorologists recognize a number of different kinds. This recognition is old-established. Edward

Clarke commented on it in 1799. 'In one day and night, you shall see fifteen or twenty different forms of snow.' The development of the snow crust itself is a winter phenomenon watched with anxiety by such people as the Lapp reindeer herders. While it is important that the crust should be sufficiently hard to bear a reindeer, it should not be too hard for a reindeer to penetrate for food. If it is too hard, the herders may fell trees so that the reindeer can feed upon their lichens.

Snow also contributes to the development of ice in that it rapidly lowers the surface temperature of the water on which it falls. It is usually critical in the final stages of icing. Clarke described its effects in the Archipelago Sea in 1799.

'The sudden effect of the snow mingling with the sea water, now cooled nearly to the point of congelation, was most striking. The water became turbid, like milk turning to curd; pieces of ice soon made their appearance . . . the floating masses rapidly assumed a compact shape . . . the whole passage frozen overnight.'

Visually, snow is the element of winter which gives uniformity to the scene. It covers land, water and swamp alike. Snow and ice together contrive to give to Finland different and smoother contours in winter from those which prevail in summer.

### The Advance and Retreat of the Ice Frontier

The ice frontier advances horizontally over the inland waterways and surrounding seas. It also penetrates vertically into the ground. Frost, often continuous frost, usually establishes itself before the occurrence of snowfall. A country saying attests that by 27 November an ice lid has been put on the lake and by 30 November there is enough snow to drive by sleigh. (*Anttri (30. XI) aisoilla ajaa, Kaija (27. XI) kansia valaa.*) The sheath of ice, which changes the form and function of most water areas, is of critical concern for much human activity. As a result, the dates of transformation are among some of the earliest and most assiduously recorded meteorological features.

The advance and retreat of the ice frontier is critical in a second sense. Even in detail, the transformation is rarely a sudden process. It takes place over several weeks. This means that there are periods when the ice neither bears nor breaks. The resulting personal hazards and inconveniences are exaggerated because of the intricate land and water relationships which characterize Finland. The inhabitants of the extensive archipelagoes off the coasts of Finland are painfully aware of their isolation during the autumn and spring seasons of *kelirikko* (Sw. *menföre*). January brings the certainty of firm midwinter ice. Unfortunately, it is not possible to have the assurance and relative moderation of January without suffering the immoderation of February's nadir. As an old Nousiainen proverb puts it – *Jos iso tammi helpottaa niin pikku tammi kiristää* – if big January makes things easier, little January (i.e. February) makes things harder.

### (a) Ice and the Inland Waters

The advance and retreat of the ice frontier hangs upon the persistence of temperatures at or below freezing point and is consequently a direct result of the

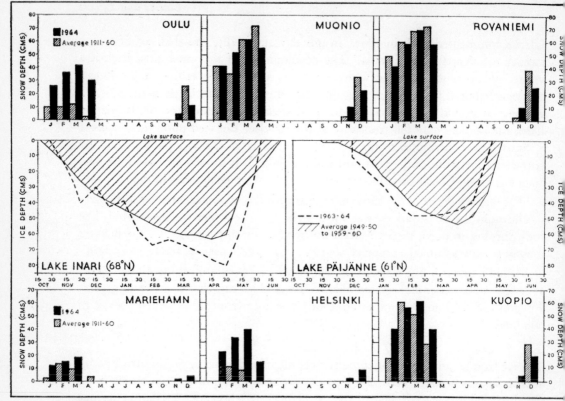

**Figure 6**

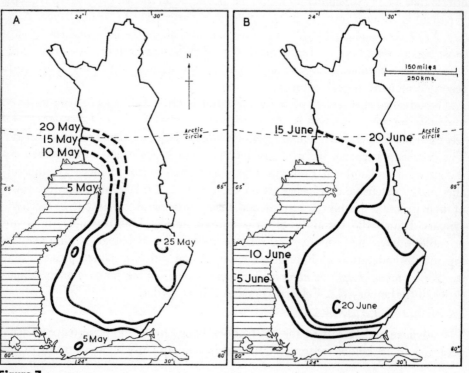

**Figure 7**

conditions summarized in Figures 3 and 4. The submission of the varied water masses to ice depends upon snowfall and wind conditions as well as their shapes, depths and patterns of circulation. Generally speaking, bays and shallows will freeze before rivers. The larger and deeper lakes may lack a continuous ice cover in milder winters. The thaw takes place a week or two earlier along rivers than upon lakes – earlier, sometimes, than the ice melt around the coasts. Figure 3 provides the general picture of the advance of the ice frontier. Figure 7A shows the average dates of disappearance of lake ice. It is based upon the mean figures for the years 1892–1941 [10].

The average experiences over a period of ten winters for two sample lakes are summarized in the centre of Figure 6. The diagram shows the monthly development of lake ice for south Finnish and north Finnish recording stations. By February and March, a minimum thickness of 60 cms. and a maximum of 80 cms. have developed on the surface of most lakes in northern Finland [11]. The four-month growth of ice disappears in as many weeks from the end of April onwards. In south Finland, ice depths average a minimum thickness of 40 cms., but depths of 80 cms. are recorded. The ice break-up begins in mid-April.

Figure 7A shows that lake ice persists over fully half of Finland until mid-May. Lake ice disappears more slowly than snow, but more quickly than ground frost.

The most exceptional situation known has been reconstructed by J. M. Angervo in Figure 7B. It shows the dates of disappearance of ice in 1867, the year of the last great famine in Finland. The map indicates that not only was lake ice still intact over most of Finland well into June, but that the southern lake district was only released of its ice about a week before midsummer. Such a prolongation of winter is a national disaster.

## (b) *Frost in the Ground*

The penetration of frost into the ground is a winter phenomenon which has long attracted the attention of the Finns. They have their own word for ground frost (*tuollu* or *routa*, Sw. *tjäle*) and the Lapps have a variant of it. The depth of frost penetration aroused the curiosity of C. C. Böcker in the 1820's and his agricultural questionnaires included items on the vertical variation of soil temperatures.

In the same way as a variety of physical circumstances affect the freezing of lake waters, so a range of factors control the penetration of frost into the soil. Among them, soil structure, soil water content and soil acidity play leading roles.

**Figure 6. Snow and Inland Ice Conditions for north and south Finland**
The diagram is based on *The Monthly Review of Weather Conditions of the Central Meteorological Institute of Finland, 1964*. Six stations are indicated for snowfall: the mean conditions for 1911–60 are juxtaposed with those of 1964. The centre of the diagram shows the development of lake ice for 1963–4. (Source: Central Hydrological Bureau)

**Figure 7. Disappearance of Lake Ice**
Map A indicates the average date of disappearance of lake ice for the period 1892–1941. Map B, the exceptional condition in 1867, the year of the last great famine in Finland. (Source: J. M. Angervo, *Lyhyt sääoppi ja säänennustajan opas,* Keuruu, 1962)

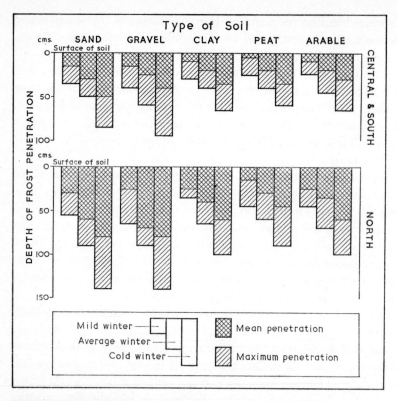

**Figure 8. Mean and Maximum Depths of Frost Penetration in Various Soils**

(Based on S. Huovila and S. E. Pihlajavaara, *Valtion Teknillinen Tutkimuslaitos Tiede,* III, 2, 1956)

The time of occurrence and nature of snowfall are also important. For example, if snow accumulates on unfrozen ground, it may cause considerable damage to underlying crops and may hamper transport. Figure 8 indicates mean and maximum depths of frost penetration in different soils.

Ground frost itself has a different expression in different types of soil. For example, the length of ice crystals varies, largely as a result of porosity. Crystals may be as short as 2–4 cms. in clay soils; 5–7 cms. in peaty soils and as much as 20 cms. in sand. Ground frost may also assume the form of banded layers. The form as well as the depth of ground frost affect the duration and nature of the thaw. In the hard winter of 1959–60, for the country at large, ground frost took over nine weeks to thaw. In the northern part of the country, it averaged fully twelve weeks. Usually it takes a much shorter time. In north Finland in exceptionally hard winters, frost may remain in the ground throughout the summer; but its occurrence is very sporadic. Finland has no permafrost area in the accepted sense of the term.

In the higher fell country, frost plays an active erosional role in its own right and frost shattering of exposed rocks is widespread [12]. Although the form of shattering depends on the type of rock, it is closely related to the length of the periods of freeze-and-thaw. When summer comes, the work of winter stands exposed on the fell slopes in the shape of scree accumulations, stone 'streams', stone 'rivers'; while, on the open ground, stones and pebbles arrange themselves in the deformed rings and stripes commonly associated with the deep freeze of sub-Arctic winters.

## (c) *Ice and the Surrounding Seas*

While the freezing of inland waters and the blanketing of the land with snow are winter features known to many lands, the submission of Finland's coastal waters to winter icing is a more uncommon feature. The entire Finnish coast is encircled with ice to a greater or lesser extent throughout the winter. When a sufficient number of degrees of frost have accumulated, ice-producing elements win their battle over ice-resisting elements. Given the intensity of frost, it would be possible to calculate the number of frost days required to give rise to this situation; but the period of ice-generation is very variable. For example, if weather conditions result in temperatures above zero in the ice-generating period, the formation of sea ice will be delayed. If snowfall occurs at a critical stage, the surface temperature of the water will be lowered and the freeze may be hastened. In winters of exceptional severity, the shallows of the Bothnian Bay may freeze in mid-October and the archipelago channels of the Gulf of Finland by the end of November.

While lowering of temperature is the principal cause of sea ice, a number of other physical controls play a part. The first is the shape and character of the Baltic Sea. Finland's coastal waters belong to the innermost basins of a virtually closed sea. The form of the basins to the south and west of Finland affect the transport and exchange of their water with the Central Baltic [13]. The morphology of the Bothnian Sea, which is divided from the Central Baltic by two shallow sills between the Åland archipelago and the Swedish coast, is especially influential. The Bothnian Sea, fed by a large number of rivers draining an extensive catchment area, discharges its brackish waters into the Central Baltic. The intervening rock sills restrict the reciprocal movement of water from the south. The Åland Sea, which reaches depths of 200m., contains water of higher salt content.

The formation of sea ice is affected by salinity. The salt content of the surface water diminishes from 10 grams per litre in the Danish sound, to 6 grams per litre in the Åland Sea and 2 grams at the heads of the two gulfs. Salinity increases with depth, the highest percentage in the Central Baltic occurring below 100m. Of especial interest in this context is the advective transport of water, with corresponding heat exchanges at different levels in the water. The advection currents in Finland's offshore waters, about which relatively little is known, are probably critical in submission or resistance to icing.

Because of its virtually tideless character, currents in the Baltic Sea are highly important in the development of ice distribution. In the absence of tides, varia-

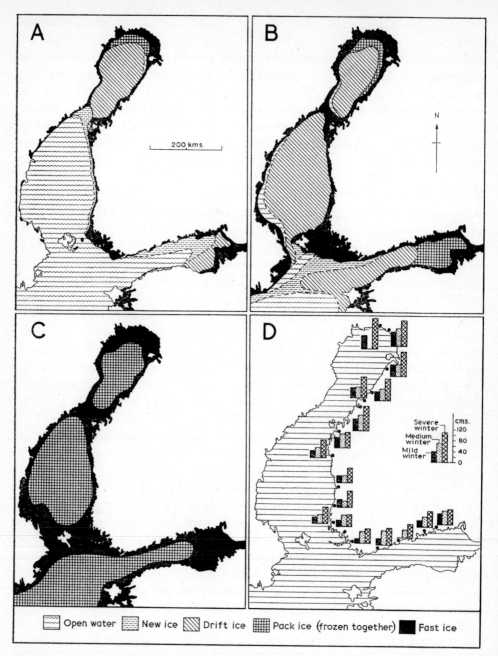

**Figure 9. Sea Ice Conditions around the Finnish Coast**

The maps indicate a mild winter (A), an average winter (B) and a hard winter (C). D shows the average thickness of ice at the approaches to Finland's principal ports in a mild, a hard and an average winter. (Based on R. Jurva, *Ice Atlas,* Helsinki, 1937)

tions in the level of the Baltic are principally due to changes in atmospheric pressure and to wind direction [14]. These variations also have their own effects on local and regional ice distributions which in turn are closely related to the nature of the sheltering skerry zones.

In open waters, the study of wind strengths and directions – prevailing and intermittent – is vital for understanding the formation and development of ice. In November and early December, for example, a prolonged south-west wind can delay the freezing of Finland's Bothnian coasts for a full fortnight. Contrastingly, an east wind in January can ease the situation in Finnish territorial waters at the expense of piling up drift ice along the Swedish coast (as happened in the winter of 1965–6). The direction of March winds is especially critical for the south coast, for they control the circulation of water in the Gulf of Finland and the consequent movement of ice fields and drift ice. Wind direction will largely determine the opening and closing of sea lanes. Figure 16 provides a precise illustration reflected in the strenuous activity recorded in the logbook of the ice-breaker *Sisu* in March, 1963.

The distribution of ice over Finland's surrounding seas varies according to the severity of the winter. The frequency of occurrence of different types of winter from the standpoint of sea ice is summarized in Figure 10. The diagram, compiled by Risto Jurva, covers the period 1850–1950 and indicates the extent of sea ice in thousands of square kilometres. It will be observed that the century included thirteen exceptionally hard winters, in each of which fully 400,000 square kilometres of the Baltic were frozen over. The contrasting figures for the mild winters were 60,000 square kilometres. Hard winters imply a greater depth as well as a greater extent of sea ice and they are critical for Finland [15].

Figure 9 summarizes the ice situations for a mild winter (A), an average winter (B) and a hard winter (C). Naturally, there are many different varieties of ice; but in the interests of clarity only four principal kinds are defined. Ice is first identified as a film no more than several millimetres thick and remarkably elastic in its response to the movement of the waters. The ice skin is frequently succeeded by pancake-shaped formations (F. *lautasjää*; Sw., *tallriksis*). 'Pancake' ice may be 5–10 cms. in thickness. In protected coastal waters these young ice formations are swiftly converted into fast ice. In the open sea, they are readily compacted by wind and water movement. If there are calm conditions, fast ice may extend far into the open sea. Drift ice in the open sea, 10 cms. or more thick, may raft to form layered ice and may be converted into solid ice fields many square kilometres in extent. In hard winters, an ice bridge may form over the narrows of the Åland Sea [16]. The more frequent development of the Quarken ice bridge is closely related to the varying depths of underwater rocks and shoals.

The different types of winter have their local impact as well as their general expression. Figure 9 (D) illustrates the depth of sea ice at the principal Finnish harbours in mild, medium and severe winters. In the most acutely affected har-bours at the head of the Bothnian Gulf, the thickness of sea ice varies from as

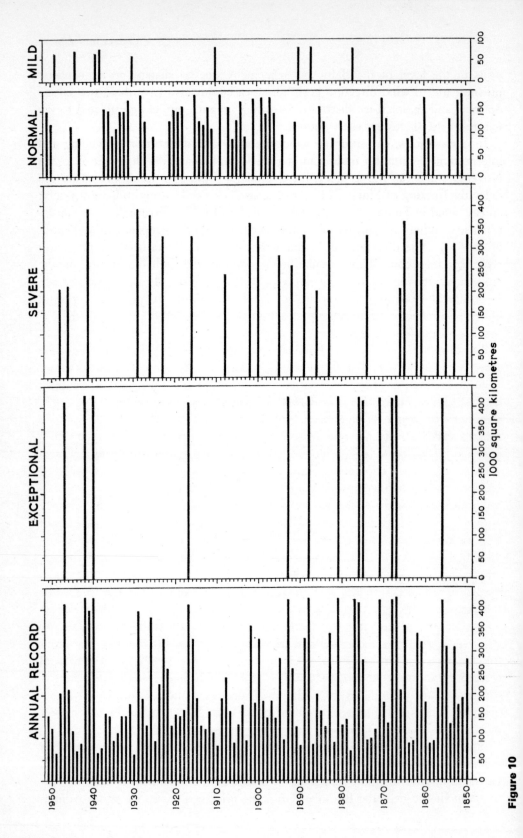

**Figure 10**

46

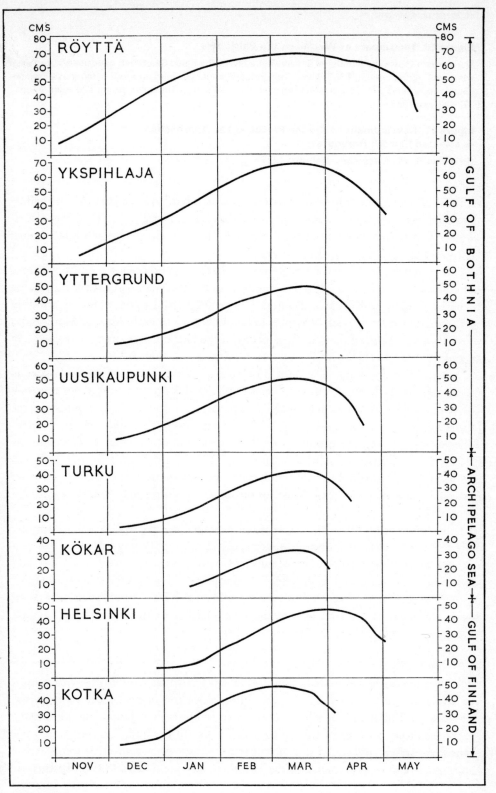

**Figure 11**

**Figure 10. The Impact of Winter on the Baltic Sea**

The diagram shows the number of square kilometres of the Baltic Sea which have been frozen each winter during the century 1850–1950. The annual record is divided into four categories of winter. (Based on R. Jurva, On the variations and changes of freezing in the Baltic during 120 years, *Fennia,* 72, Helsinki, 1952)

**Figure 11. Development of the Ice Profile at the Approaches to selected Finnish Harbours**

(Based on R. Jurva, *Ice Atlas,* Helsinki, 1937)

little as 40 cms. in a mild winter to 120 cms. in a hard winter [17]. About half of the thickness of sea ice consists of partly thawed and frozen snow on top of sea-water. The normal curves of ice development for the approaches to eight Finnish harbours are illustrated in Figure 11.

The extent of ice to be traversed between harbours and open sea is also a feature of concern to navigators. The average figures for the years 1934–53 indicate that a harbour such as Kotka or Hamina is separated from open water by roughly 200 kms. of ice at the peak of winter in late February or early March. Along more than three-quarters of the sea-route between the harbour and open water, ice will exceed 10 cms. in thickness.

Sea ice is a dynamic substance. The waxing and waning of the ice cover is correspondingly lively. Drift ice, for example, builds up pressures along the zone of contact with fast ice. Ice ridges result. Storms can produce impressive ice thrusting. Along the fringes of the fast ice, ridges up to 6m. high may be formed. The element of exaggeration given by Skjöldebrand in Plate 3 is excusable. Because of its dynamic qualities, sea ice is also an erosional agent. It rides up on to the land, 'tulips' around shallow rock outcrops and transports boulders over surprising distances. Ice blocks thrust up on to skerry shores may remain until mid-summer.

The culmination of the ice cover usually occurs in early March. Under normal circumstances, complete disappearance takes about eighty days. Most of the fast ice has a cover of snow. In late March and April this begins to melt by day and freeze by night to produce treacherous conditions. Most sea ice rots from above as well as dissolving from below. At the end of a hard winter, such as that of 1942, ice floes may still be seen in the inner reaches of the Finnish Gulf in late May; in the inner Bothnian Bay, in mid-June.

## The Silhouette of Finland

The primary cause behind the combined effects known as winter is the diminution of heat received from solar radiation. The proportion of heat received from the sun in south Finland in the midwinter months of December, January and February is three to four per cent of the annual total. In north Finland, it is one to two per cent. The arrival and departure of winter are summed up respectively in the disappearance and re-appearance of the sun, the consequent fall and rise of tempera-

1. Helsinki in Winter (from P. Gaimard, *Voyage de la Commission Scientifique du Nord en Scandinavie, Atlas Historique*, Paris, 1943–8).
2. 'A Laplander descending a mountain on his snow skates', as drawn by D. Dighton for A. de Capell Brooke, *A Winter in Lapland and Sweden*, London, 1827.

3. A Journey through Aland's pack ice (from L. Belanger in J. Acerbi, *Travels through Sweden, Finland and Lapland*, London, 1802).

4. Aurora borealis (from A. F. Skiöldebrand, *A Picturesque Journey to the North Cape*, London, 1813).

5. *Halla*, by Hugo Simberg (1873–1917), a symbolic representation of summer frost.

6. Street in Helsinki on a winter morning, 1868, by Magnus von Wright (Art Gallery of Ateneum, Helsinki).

ture, the advance and retreat of the ice frontier and the advance and retreat of the snow frontier.

Translated into human terms, all of this means that the Finns spend half of their lives coping with a country which, under its mantle of ice and snow, is a silhouette of itself. Yet, while they are sensitive to all of the manifestations of winter that touch their daily round, they are more than game to meet the challenge. The success of the Finns in counteracting the peremptory demands of winter lies in their ability to benefit from the material techniques of the twentieth century, their growing capacity for finding enjoyment in the brighter elements of the winter scene and the sense of national achievement which they experience in overcoming the physical hardships of their land. To paraphrase Toivo Pekkanen's wintry novel, 'Everything may appear to be dead and frozen . . . but the force of life is extremely tough. It may retreat to the very marrow of the bones, but it can wait there for a long time' [18].

# BIBLIOGRAPHY

[1] The principal sources employed in the construction of the temperature maps in this chapter have been the records of the Central Meteorological Institute of Finland for the period 1931–60. They were kindly supplied by Dr. J. M. Angervo, Dr. O. Kolkki and Maisteri Liukka. Additional maps of a relevant character are found in the *Atlases of Finland*, 1899, 1910, 1925 and 1960, with their accompanying texts.

[2] *Skrifter och brev*, II, Stockholm, 1925, p. 74.

[3] The two sources used in this section are J. Hautala, *Vanhat merkkipäivät*, Helsinki, 1948, and K. Vilkuna, *Vuotuinen ajantieto*, Helsinki, 1950.

[4] *Les Hivers dans l'Europe occidentale*, Leyden, 1928.

[5] J. Blüthgen, Der Winter in Nordeuropa, *Petermanns Geographische Mitteilungen*, 1948, 92.

[6] On the constancy of the frequency of some temperature and air pressure waves, *Geophysica*, 4, 2, Helsinki, 1953.

[7] Reino Kalliola, *Suomen luonto vuodenaikojen vaihtelussa*, Porvoo, 1959.

[8] J. Säko, On the damage to fruit farming in Finland, *Maataloustieteellinen aikakauskirja*, 1957, 29, 1, 1–26.

[9] M. Seppänen, *On the accumulation and the decreasing of snow in pine-dominated forest in Finland*, Helsinki, 1961.

[10] J. M. Angervo, *Lyhyt sääoppi ja säänennustajan opas*, Keuruu, 1962.

[11] A detailed investigation of the thermal behaviour of Lake Päijänne has been made by H. Simojoki, Hydrologische und thermische Untersuchung des Sees Päijänne, *Hydrologisen toimiston tiedonantoja*, XVIII, Helsinki, 1960.

[12] B. Ohlson, Frostaktivität, Verwitterung und Bodenbildung in den Fjeldgegenden von Enontekiö, Finnisch-Lappland, *Fennia*, 89, 3, 1964.

**4**

[13] E. Palosuo, The seasonal variations of water exchange between the Baltic proper and the Gulf of Bothnia, *Publications of the Marine Research Institute*, 1964, 215.

[14] E. Lisitzin, The relations between wind, current and water level in the Gulf of Finland, *Soc. Sc. Fennica*, XIII, 6, 1946.

[15] E. Palosuo, *A treatise on severe ice conditions in the central Baltic*, Helsinki, 1953.

[16] E. Palosuo, On solid ice bridges between Finland and Sweden, *Terra*, 1956, 3, 86–96.

[17] E. Palosuo, *The Gulf of Bothnia in Winter*, I *Data from Winter Cruises*, Helsinki, 1964; II, *Freezing and Ice Forms*, Helsinki, 1963.

[18] Nuorin veli, 1946, *Teokset*, IV, Porvoo, 1958.

# Part 2      Solutions to the Problem

There are three principal solutions to the problems raised by winter. One is passive; two are active. Winter's cold and darkness can be met passively by seeking refuge from it. Animals seek refuge by changing their habits or habitat. Men seek protection by erecting shelters and creating artificial climates in them. They produce micro-climates about their bodies through winter clothing and they offset cold through various forms of food and drink. Winter's problems can also be met in active ways – by making a direct assault on its consequences or by treating them as an amenity in their own right. In Finland, the assault takes three different forms – the struggle with ice (especially at sea), the struggle with snow, and the attempt to break the natural darkness of winter through artificial light. Ice and snow may also be used to positive advantage. Winter is a natural season of the year for work in the forests. Historically, it was also the best time of the year for hunting and travelling. Because so much other activity was at a standstill, it was also a season of sociability. Contemporarily, it is complemented by the nationwide enjoyment of winter sporting.

The solutions to the problems of winter are inseparable from technological progress. The incidence of winter cannot be eliminated, but its burden can be eased through the changing mastery possessed over the thermal environment. In the process, new attitudes to winter emerge, and they are strengthened by philosophies which see in human history signs of a 'coldward course of progress'.

(a) *THE STRUGGLE WITH ICE*

A central fact in Finland's struggle with winter is the freezing of the Baltic Sea. The most striking feature of the struggle has been Finland's gradual success in overcoming the seasonal interruption of overseas communications. There have been three stages in the struggle – passive acceptance, active resistance and positive assault. These are a reflection of technical equipment. At the same time a pragmatic approach to the problem of interruption has changed to a wholly scientific attitude. The constraints of winter ice have been broken with the aid of three technical innovations – the application of steam and internal combustion to sea-going shipping, the employment of steel plating for ships' hulls, and the use of telegraphic and radio communications. The first two have been combined in the construction of ice-breakers and ice-strengthened ships; the third has enabled the rapid assembly of information for synoptic ice charts and the fore-casting of weather conditions.

*The Birth of Winter Shipping*

In the days of the sailing ship, the closure of Finland's ports in winter was passively accepted. There were, of course, isolated instances where temporal power challenged physical authority. For example, in January 1721, Lord Polwarth was informed that the Czar intended 'to break up the ice in the Finnish sheers so as to make use of his galleys in the winter'. During the period of winter ice, ship-ping contacts ceased, beacons were extinguished and links were often reduced to those of the hazardous ice boat. These were employed, for example, on the post route from Åland's Eckerö to mainland Sweden's Grisslehamn. The boats employed, of which an example is kept in the post museum at Eckerö, were 5·6 metres long and 1·8 metres broad with almost flat bottoms. They had a crew of six men, who hauled or sailed the boat as occasion demanded in a manner which could not be used by either a normal boat or a normal sledge. A system of 'optical telegraphs' and of cannon shots was devised to inform the post boat operators. An agreement between Sweden and Russia in 1810 arranged for one 24 pound cannon shot to be fired from Grisslehamn and Signilskär if ice interrupted the passage; two shots, as soon as the passage was clear [1].

Only the establishment of reliable ice bridges across the narrows of the Quarken or, less frequently, across the Åland Sea brought a degree of certainty to extra-territorial communications. A review of the situation conducted by Finland's first ice-breaker commission [2] observed that in the 88 years following 1816, sleigh traffic over the Baltic to Sweden had been possible during 23 winters. The ice bridge of 1871 is memorable because the post was conveyed by horse and sleigh from Eckerö to the Swedish mainland from 4 February to 10 March. In 1893 butter exports travelled across the Quarken from Vaasa to Umeå, while during the Winter War of 1940, motor vehicles carried a variety of commodities over the same route.

The introduction of steam power carried with it the immediate prospect of increased manoeuvrability in the face of ice. It aided speedier escape in the absence of wind, easier exploitation of open shipping lanes and the prospect of bringing greater power to bear upon frozen surfaces.

In October 1836, Finland acquired its first steamship, the *Prince Menschikoff*. A second, *Storfursten*, was purchased from Britain the following year. To the same period belong the first American experiments in using steamships to combat ice – the *Ice King* on the Hudson river in 1836 and the *City Ice Boat* of Philadelphia on the Delaware in 1837. But, in its earlier stages of development, the use of the steamship did not greatly affect trafficking in wider expanses of seasonally frozen waters, for knowledge about the nature and behaviour of sea ice was needed as well as improved vessels [3].

A change of mood was effected in some circles by the exploits of A. E. Nordenskiöld. His successful adventures with the *Sofia* in the Arctic Ocean around Spitzbergen and along the coast of Greenland stimulated interest in winter travel through Baltic waters. After all, the *Sofia* had been built for the winter run between Stockholm and Baltischport on the Estonian coast. Somewhat later, in the same way as the Greenland crossing by Fritjof Nansen opened new prospects for the use of the ski, so A. E. Nordenskiöld's circumnavigation of the Old World in the *Vega* by way of the North-East Passage demonstrated the possibilities of navigating ice-covered seas. Nearer at hand, Russian experiences around the naval base at Kronstadt and Swedish success on the Västervik-Visby route after 1858 encouraged Finnish enterprise. In Finland, discussion grew livelier in the 1860's.

There were those who dismissed 'winter traffic on the sixtieth parallel as a dream'. There were the more sanguine who rightly emphasized that winter navigation in the Central Baltic area should not be so difficult as it was generally presented. There were the enthusiasts who were already looking for a winter harbour. Mariehamn had come into existence in 1861; but it was too far removed from mainland Finland to function successfully as a winter port. Thoughts on Hangö as the most suitable mainland winter port had already been formally expressed in 1861. However, experiment with the steamship *Postiljonen*, which sailed for the first time on 24 November 1870, over the historic post route between Grisslehamn and Eckerö, confirmed the doubts of the pessimists. In the meantime, the optimists who continued to advocate Hangö had no scientific evidence to prove that the short route across the Åland Sea was not necessarily the most ice free route. So *Postiljonen* continued from 1870 onwards, employing *in extremis* all the antique devices hitherto used for combating ice – clubs, hatchets and saws as well as dynamite. Landwards, a railway line was struck from Helsinki to Hangö in 1872–3.

The real beginning of regular winter navigation between Finland and the outer world dates from 1876. In that year, the *Express* began its Hangö-Stockholm journeys. In 1877, the *Express* was winter-strengthened. But, even then, it was incapable of dealing with ice thicker than 12–15 centimetres. In 1878, *Express* initiated a weekly sailing from 15 November–15 May. In the same year, a government subsidy confirmed faith in the vessel. The regulation sailing time was 17 hours, though *Express* had sometimes to struggle for days to make the passage. In 1881, 1888, 1889 and 1893, it had to curtail operations, despite the fact that its horse-power had been augmented.

*Express* carried both passenger and commodity traffic. Butter and paper were accompanied by ordinary travellers and emigrants. As many as 1500 passengers travelled annually during the winter seasons of the late 1880's. Karl Tavastjerna had immortalized the arrival of *Express* in Stockholm in his poem, *Transitofart* [4].

> Och det växer fram ett skeppskrov,
>     rimmigt, frostigt vitt,
> frusande i moln av ånga, nästan bortskymt titt.
> Vitförsilvrat tågverk blänker av
>     millioner iskristaller,
> när ifrån elektrisk lampa spökvitt
>     sken på prakten faller.
> Vinterångaren från Finland!
>     Emigranter, post . . .

Given a winter harbour, a railroad binding it to the capital and overseas demands for Finland's products, the scale and reliability of winter shipping links came under closer inspection. The increased trade which had grown up in the summer months exaggerated the contrast with winter operations. Debate centred on the means of strengthening trade from November to May. Two possibilities presented themselves – to employ an outport such as Copenhagen or to establish an icebreaker service.

An icebreaker commission was set up in 1889 to consider the matter. Other countries had already provided evidence of the value of icebreaker services. Ice-breakers had been used with considerable effect on the Elbe since 1872, in Norway since 1876, in Denmark since 1881 and in Sweden since 1882. The commission analysed their performances and working costs. *Bryderen* from Copenhagen, came to give a practical demonstration and effectively wooed the Finns to the idea of purchasing icebreakers of their own. In their discussions, the members of the commission called on the advice and experience of A. E. Nordenskiöld. Eventually, a vessel was commissioned from Stockholm and it came to Helsinki under the name of *Murtaja* on 1 April 1890. It was described as 'the newest, biggest and strongest icebreaker in Europe'. Its maximum horsepower was 1,600. *Murtaja* was a conventional vessel, though unconventional models were also discussed in the literature of the day. Two remarkable examples were G. E. Boethius's ice-breaker (which was provided with three circular saws, each three metres in diameter, and four heavy donkey engines behind them) and Bovy's icebreaking apparatus (which combined the principle of the circular saw and the steam-hammer). Conventional though it might be, *Murtaja* was enough to open a new chapter in the story of Finland's struggle with winter ice.

## Broadening the Base of Winter Shipping

With Hangö established as Finland's winter port, a regular line to Hull in being and an icebreaker to hand, the next stage was to broaden the basis of operations and to extend continuous – or near continuous – winter navigation to other har-bours. At this stage, the expert advice of Finland's growing range of natural scientists was increasingly sought. Trans-Atlantic experiences were also investigated and a parallel situation to that of the Central Baltic was sought on the Upper Great Lakes. Navigational experiences from the Mackinac Sound were cited and new types of icebreaker from North America were debated. The new technical possibilities quickened interest in the winter trading prospects of a number of ports. Åland was discussed more fully. Nystad was proposed. Raumo was listed as a possibility, though the two outports of Pori (Mäntyluoto and Räfsö) were regarded as more favourable. At this time, Turku was considered too far inland to keep open.

But the more energetic harbour authorities did not wait upon the action of central authority. Turku set the fashion by acquiring its own icebreaker tug in 1898 and the other principal harbours between Viipuri (Viborg) and Raumo speedily followed suit. As ice-strengthened ocean-going vessels multiplied, the icebreaker's function assumed a more complementary character. Turku was par-ticularly sensitive to the winter rivalry of the new harbour at Hangö, but the distance from Stockholm to Turku is a tenth shorter than that from Stockholm to Hangö. After 1900, a considerable struggle developed between the two ports to control winter traffic to Stockholm, but once Turku's winter fairway was successfully established, it rapidly acquired winter precedence over the new port.

Those who sought to broaden the basis of winter-going shipping aimed at attracting a growing number of foreign vessels as well as keeping harbours open for Finnish shipping. While locally owned small icebreakers might undertake the responsibility of dealing with the entry to and exit from their home ports, vessels of the national icebreaker service were likely to be faced with rescue operations outside territorial waters. The icebreaker commission was supplied with details of the type of operation in which icebreakers might be called upon. In 1888, for example, the *Juana Nancy* had been imprisoned in pack ice from 16 January to 5 June, seven miles north of Ulkokalla light in the Bothnian Gulf; while in 1881, the *Silvio* had been ice-bound for 105 days. To prevent such incidents would reduce the reluctance of foreign vessels to enter Finnish waters in winter.

The ability of icebreakers to cope with this type of situation was strengthened by changes in the construction of icebreakers. New patterns of power were emerging to change the nature of the assault on winter ice. Already before the end of the century, British shipyards were constructing icebreakers capable of generating 10,000 horsepower. The new prospects of security which became apparent automatically eased winter trading. Between 1900–15, for example, the volume of paper products alone which were exported during winter multiplied by three.

The degree of risk involved was given tangible expression in insurance premiums. Additional premiums were required of vessels entering the Baltic in winter except in the case of acceptably ice-strengthened ships. Ice-strengthening was another modification which helped to broaden the base of winter shipping. Strengthening spread from icebreakers to passenger vessels and finally to cargo shipping.

Ice-strengthening is achieved principally by the use of thicker steel plating on the hull. Shipping underwriters, such as Lloyd's and *Norske Veritas*, have developed a classification of winter-strengthened hulls. They recognize a series of grades which run from 1A (which involves a 10% increase in hull weight), through 1B (a 4% increase) to 1C (a 2% increase). A super-class has also been added (with a 12% increase). The classification has been largely derived from the Finnish system of grading ice-strengthening. Vessels may also be fitted with icebreaker bows, with specially strengthened rudder shafts and propeller shafts, and with 'ice-frames' (specially designed panels fitted into the hull of the ship to increase its resistance to stress). In the struggle with ice, the power of the engine in relation to the build of the ship is a primary consideration. Winter strengthening amounts to a substantial capital outlay, but it yields a reduction of insurance premiums. It is also taken into consideration in assessing the tax imposed on vessels entering Finnish harbours between 1 December and 30 April. Super class and 1A vessels pay no tax; Classes 1B and 1C, 15 and 33 marks per registered ton; Class II (which conforms to winter trafficking conditions, but is not ice-strengthened), 33 marks; Class III (which does not conform to winter trafficking requirements), 60 marks [5].

## The Growth of the Icebreaker Fleet

In former times, Finnish shipping of any consequence left home waters during the winter months and engaged in carrying trade between foreign harbours until the reopening of the Baltic. The winter practice of tramping between North Sea and Mediterranean ports is generously recorded in the collections of log books assembled in the maritime museums of Turku and Mariehamn.

When Finland became an independent country, the need to strengthen continuous overseas communications acquired a new urgency. The eastern frontier became a virtually closed frontier and much trade had to be re-oriented. In the 1930's less than 5% of Finland's foreign trade moved across land frontiers. At the same time, the facilities of the harbours of the extreme south-west soon proved inadequate to deal with the mounting trade of independent Finland. The rail network, mostly single track, was not built to serve a traffic flow oriented to a few ports, nor could the motor lorry do more than supplement the railway for bulky exports. The nature and distribution of Finland's industry is such that the larger the number of harbours that can be kept open and the longer they can operate, the more smoothly overland transport links can function.

In the early stages of its investment in icebreakers, Finland had insufficient capital to purchase abroad a fleet adequate to meet its ideal needs; but it followed technical developments in icebreakers closely and, with each successive purchase, invested in the latest designs and innovations. To *Murtaja* was added *Sampo* from Newcastle-upon-Tyne in 1898. *Sampo* took into account American experiments and added a fore propellor to help wash away the broken ice. *Apu* (from Kiel in 1899) and *Tarmo* (from Newcastle in 1907) preceded the more impressive *Jääkarhu* (from Rotterdam in 1926). In *Jääkarhu*, generation was switched from coal to oil. Oil enabled a greater range of sailing without refuelling. *Jääkarhu* required 2,600 tons of oil during its operating season, as against rather more than 3,000 tons of solid fuel needed for *Tarmo*, its coal-burning counterpart. It was also provided with so-called heeling tanks, on port and starboard sides. By transferring water from one side to the other, a heeling motion (from 5°–8°) could be produced which helped to loosen the ship when in the midst of thick ice. *Sisu*, built in 1939, featured a third improvement. It employed diesel electric machinery, which endowed it with greater manoeuvrability and direct control of the propellors from the bridge. It was also the first significant icebreaker constructed in Finland and, for this reason, heralded a new era.

## The Development of Icebreaker Construction [6]

Finns have always been interested in shipbuilding. With the advance of their shipbuilding industry and with the demand for the expansion and renewal of

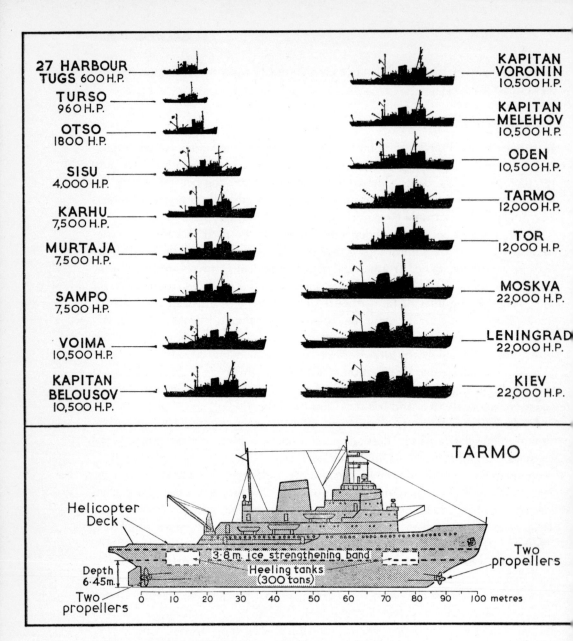

**Figure 12. The Principal Types of Icebreaker constructed in Hietalahti (Sandviken) Yards, Helsinki**

(Based on information supplied by O. Y. Värtsilä-Koncernen A. B.)

the icebreaker fleet, it was natural that they should turn their attention to the construction of icebreakers. Within a generation, they have acquired sufficient expertise in their production to be included among the world's foremost specialists. Finland is interested in the construction of all three types of icebreaker – harbour tugs, 'temperate latitude' vessels (for operation in the Baltic Sea, St. Lawrence estuary and Great Lakes) and Arctic vessels.

The vessels have been and continue to be built principally at the Hietalahti (Sandviken) shipyard in Helsinki. The yard is run by *Värtsilä-Koncernen*, a successor to a metallurgical company founded in 1834. The company now has ramifications throughout Finnish industry. As early as 1924, a Reval-built icebreaker had been converted at Sandviken into the *Voima*. A modest steam icebreaker, *Otso* of 1800 horsepower, left the yards in 1936. The diesel electric *Sisu* of 4,000 horsepower was launched on the eve of the war. Russian war reparations took their toll of Finland's icebreaker fleet in 1944. The old *Voima* (now sailing as *Malygrin*) and *Jääkarhu* (now sailing as *Sibiriakov*) were ceded to the U.S.S.R. Between 1945–55, and partly in response to the war reparations programme, Värtsilä constructed 27 harbour icebreakers. They were small in size (600 horsepower), but provided considerable experience in specialized construction. The icebreaker building activities of Värtsilä are shown in Figure 12.

In both the U.S.A. and Canada, icebreaker development continued during the war, though emphasis was placed on larger-scale vessels for Arctic (and eventually Antarctic) use. When Finland settled for its first significant post-war icebreaker, it took as its model the *Abgeweit*, a vessel designed for operation in the Northumberland straits between the Canadian provinces of New Brunswick and Prince Edward Island. The *Abgeweit*, built in 1947, operates in ice conditions which closely resemble those around Finland's coasts. It employs the four propellor principle – two fore and two aft, with the possibility of distributing its 12,000 horsepower between them as required. The new *Voima*, of 10,500 horsepower, was built after this prototype in 1953.

The measure of its recognition was an immediate order for three sister vessels by the U.S.S.R. and a fourth by Sweden. The Soviet ships, of the so-called *Kapitan* class, were delivered in 1954, 1955 and 1956. They were designed principally for use in the White Sea. *Oden* was delivered to Sweden in 1957. Three Finnish vessels followed between 1958–60 – *Karhu*, *Murtaja* and *Sampo* (all of 7,500 horsepower). The old *Murtaja* was withdrawn after 68 years of service. Some of the work on these vessels, e.g. *Oden*, was conducted at Turku in the Värtsilä Crichton-Vulcan yards.

Size and power continued to increase with the *Tarmo* built for Finnish service in 1963–4. This sister ship for *Oden*, of 12,000 horsepower, was constructed as a subordinate undertaking to the production of three 22,000 horsepower vessels ordered by the U.S.S.R. for use in polar waters. *Moskva* was delivered in 1960; *Leningrad*, in 1962; *Kiev*, in 1965. All three vessels have a displacement of 15,340 m. tons against 4,890 tons of *Tarmo*. They are the world's second most powerful icebreakers. Russia's atomic-powered *Lenin*, developing 44,000 horse-power, is exceptional.

Sandviken dock is relatively small; but its output in this field during the last decade has given to it world leadership.

## The Function and Structure of Icebreakers

The physical processes of the assault by shipping on Baltic ice, reduced to their mathematical formulae, are the province of the marine engineer. But it is relevant to pay attention to the basic situations with which an icebreaker is expected to cope. These situations are reflected in features of its construction, which again spring from the area of its operation. All in all, an icebreaker is very much a detailed response to its operational environment.

The simplest situation is one in which an icebreaker is expected to break ice at constant speed. Ice yields to the pressure of the hull principally by splitting radially, partly by bending. Vessels of the *Voima* group should be theoretically capable of moving through '10 cm. of ice at 13 knots, 20 cm. at 11 knots, 50 cm. at 7 knots, 100 cm. at $4\frac{1}{2}$ knots and 150 cm. at 3 knots'. The maximum thickness of ice which a vessel such as *Voima* could break would be about 2·5 metres.

A second situation presents itself when a vessel can no longer cleave a passage through ice and a running attack must be made on it. The icebreaker then operates as a ram – withdrawing a certain distance and making a direct assault full steam ahead.

A third situation arises when an icebreaker is confronted with pack ice. This is one of the forms of ice most frequently encountered in the Baltic Sea. It is also one of the most difficult to negotiate. Pack ice is mobile – in the broader sense that entire fields of it continuously shift in location and shape; and in the narrower sense that it changes its form within the ambit of the vessel. It is an advantage for icebreakers intended for use in pack ice to have two fore propellors, because they give greater manoeuvrability.

Icebreakers are relatively broad in relation to their length. Their beam determines the width of the channel that they cut and accordingly controls the type of merchant shipping that they can assist. Their length affects their manoeuvrability; their centre of gravity, their breaking power. Their protective plating, usually 40 cm. of special steel, is selected to meet the strain of icebreaking. One of the problems in planning icebreakers is the difficulty of simulating ice, snow and low temperature conditions in a laboratory.

In addition, icebreakers intended for use around the coast of Finland must be able to operate in relatively shallow waters. Propellors must be set as low as possible in the water to avoid damage by ice, and 100 cm. is about the maximum depth of firm ice encountered in the Baltic Sea. *Karhu*, *Murtaja* and *Sampo*, though big enough to help most shipping entering the Baltic, have been constructed with a sufficiently shallow draught (5·8 m.) to be able to operate in the restricted channels of the archipelago and to be able to enter the shallower

Bothnian harbours. *Tarmo* was constructed with a shallower draught than *Voima* (6·2 m.) partly for the same reasons.

Relatively shallow draught is the more important because of the increasing use of the *skärgård* fairways. These fairways are favoured because of their protection from pack ice. Among fairways which are now regularly employed are those of Helsinki, off the Porkala peninsula, those of Svensksund between Kotka and Hamina, and those through the south-western archipelago to Turku and to the south Bothnian ports. In the inner Gulf of Bothnia, the fairway between Oulu and Kemi is also used.

By their very nature, icebreakers need highly specialized equipment. The engine room of *Sisu* illustrates the international character of its origin – with components from Britain, Germany, Denmark, Sweden and France. The most important supplementary aid, but the most expensive, is the helicopter. It is invaluable for seeking out ice channels and dealing with emergency operations. *Tarmo*, the flagship of the icebreaker fleet, is able to accommodate a helicopter (see Figure 12).

## The Development of Ice Forecasting

The provision of ice situation charts is a regular feature of a number of countries which suffer from ice-bound coasts. For Finland they have been regularly produced for forty years [7]. The degree of their refinement has advanced strikingly. The charts are produced weekly for the Baltic; but with greater frequency for critical areas and for individual harbours. Their information is drawn from a great variety of sources – from operational icebreakers, individual ships, lighthouse-keepers (where lighthouses have not been closed for the winter season), military planes and civil aircraft.

Standard forms of representing various ice features have been devised and Figures 13, 14 and 15 provide illustrations of sample situations. The charts have grown out of the first simple sketches that were submitted by ships' captains in the 1890's. Situational charts have been accumulated over a sufficient number of winter seasons in order to build up a series of mathematical models against which developing situations can be tested. From a completely unknown quantity sixty years ago, the winter behaviour of the Baltic Sea becomes increasingly familiar.

In addition to the charts, daily ice reports are also compiled. These indicate for 114 Finnish coastal areas the prevailing ice conditions, the nature of ice development and the navigational situation. For each set of conditions, a series of ten observations is tabulated, so that the whole provides a succinct appraisal for navigators approaching Finnish waters. A final summary statement indicates the distribution of units of the icebreaker fleet and their availability for assistance. Returns from 114 coastal areas for Sweden and for 24 coastal areas from the U.S.S.R. (not always for the same day) enable the Finnish situation to be fitted into the broader Baltic scene.

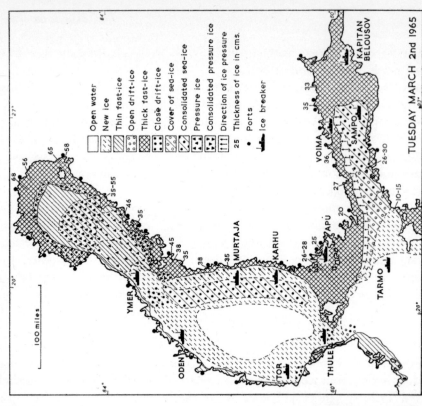

Figure 14

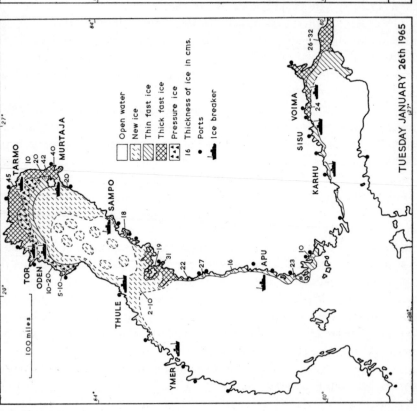

Figure 13

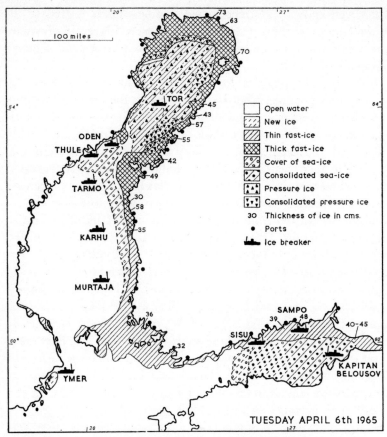

**Figures 13, 14 & 15. A Sequence of Ice Situation Charts for 1965:**
**(1) January 26, 1965. (2) March 2, 1965. (3) April 6, 1965.**
(Based on the Report of the Marine Research Institute, Helsinki)

## The Deployment of the Icebreaker Fleet

The deployment of the icebreaker fleet depends at the outset on the size and form of its units. Most icebreakers have extended operating distances (e.g. *Karhu*, 2,950 nautical miles) and most operate an average of ten hours daily at the height of the season.

Operations must be considered in two contexts. There is first the broader context – the regional movement of vessels in response to the advance and retreat of winter. Secondly, there is the movement of vessels to deal with the individual needs of shipping at particular times and places.

A number of general principles have evolved in the broader deployment of the icebreaker fleet. In the first place, deployment of vessels reflects the character of the winter. In 'open winters', operational programmes are quite different from those in closed winters. Figure 17 illustrates the movements of *Tarmo* during a mild winter, when well-known ice-strengthened trading vessels moved to the inner reaches of the Gulf of Bothnia throughout the season. Figure 16 illustrates the annual movement of *Sisu* as summarized in its log book for 1963 and depicts a more usual programme of activity.

Secondly, icebreakers are employed to delay the closure of the more ice-hampered ports as long as possible. The task is greatest at the heads of the twin gulfs. Viipuri, Finland's principal export harbour until it was ceded to the U.S.S.R. in 1944, was one of the most critical ports. The ports of the Gulf of Bothnia are accustomed to annual closure, though they expect increasingly that attempts will be made to keep them open. Figure 18 illustrates the effectiveness of delaying action by icebreakers. If it is foreseen that closure cannot be prevented, icebreaker operations are shifted from the northern ports of the Bothnian Gulf to the ports of the Bothnian Sea and from the ports of the inner Gulf of Finland to those of its more westerly shores. This operation is not realised without considerable protest from the authorities of the ports at the head of the gulfs.

Thirdly, every effort is made to keep open the principal harbours of the southwest and south coasts – from Mäntyluoto (the outport of Pori) to Kotka. Of these, Kotka experiences the greatest ice obstacles. It is also the most critical from the economic point of view because it is Finland's principal export harbour. In milder winters, 60% of Finland's exports are handled by Helsinki and Kotka, but in harder winters, the percentage falls to 40%. The 20% difference is usually complemented by the increased trade of Hangö and Turku. The harbour of Turku no longer experiences significant winter interruption of commodity traffic – an important addition to its function as Finland's principal passenger port for Stockholm. Though vessels may be rigidly confined to such channels as are kept open by icebreakers, they may still employ the pilots who take them over at other times of the year. For eyes unaccustomed to the sight, it is unusual to see a car or tractor instead of a cutter bringing the pilot to the ship's ladder.

March is the most critical month in the deployment of icebreakers during a normal or severe winter. This is because of the behaviour of sea ice in the central Baltic at that time of the year. Although channels may have been successfully maintained to Helsinki and Kotka, the movement of pack ice in the outer sea may introduce new forms of obstruction. The movements of *Sisu* in the spring of 1963 illustrates a typical reaction to this circumstance. Heavy fields of pack ice obstructing normal sailing routes through the Central Baltic may require as much care in negotiation as port entrances.

The advance of spring brings with it the final stages in the icebreaker programme. Then, the principal object is to hasten the opening of closed ports. There are two parts to the spring-time stage – first, the operations in the Bothnian Sea and those which parallel them in time as far along the Gulf of Finland as Hamina; secondly, the operations in the Gulf of Bothnia, culminating in the release of Kemi. In their relations with shipping, icebreakers conduct formal convoys in smooth and protected areas, deal with the much more tricky operation of convoying in

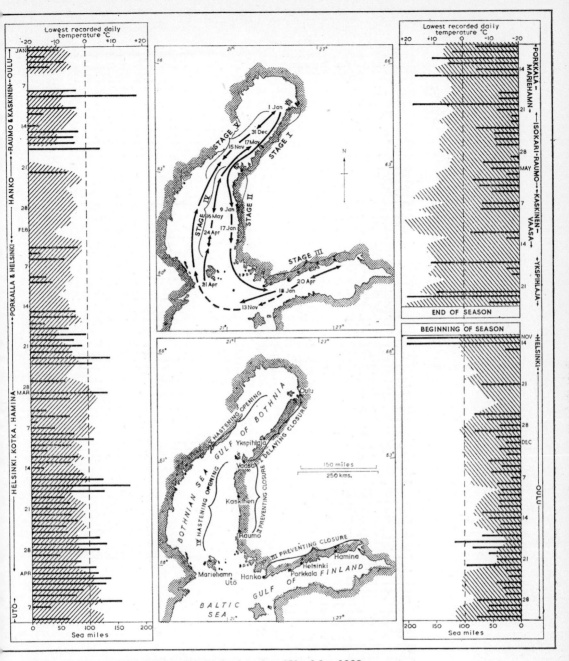

**Figure 16. Winter Operations of the Icebreaker 'Sisu' for 1963**

The diagram indicates the operational areas, the length of daily journeys made and the lowest temperature experienced each day.
(Based on the log book of *Sisu*. Kindly made available by Captain Aalto)

**Figure 17** (*overleaf*). **Winter Operations of the Icebreaker 'Tarmo' in the Winter of 1962–3**

*Tarmo* was operating exclusively in the inner reaches of the Bothnian Gulf.
(Based on the log book for *Tarmo*, 1962–3)

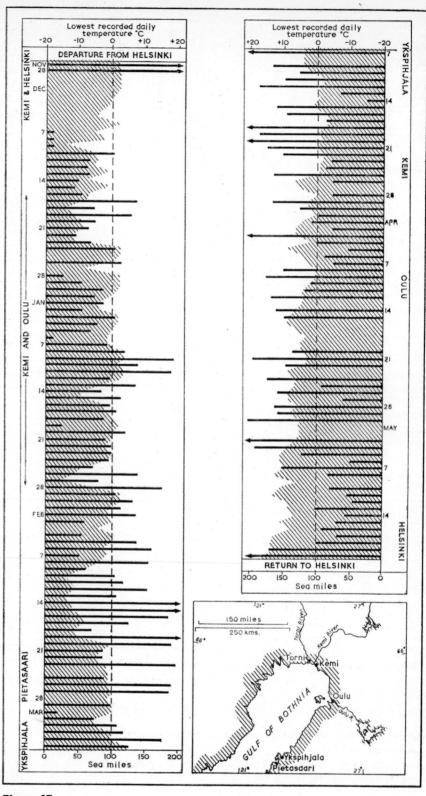

**Figure 17**

the ice fields of the open sea, and help to release icebound vessels. Through the daily ice reports, shipping is made aware of the location of icebreakers; while icebreakers' logbooks indicate the attention that is paid to the progress and disposition of trading vessels moving in precarious waters. In the circumstances prevailing in February 1966, as many as 60 or 70 vessels were requiring assistance simultaneously.

A variety of difficulties complicate winter navigation. For example, land contours are masked; pack ice accumulations introduce new contour forms; lightships are removed; buoys and seamarks no longer help; a log cannot be employed to determine distances travelled. On top of this, there is a longer period of darkness to contend with so that searchlights are needed. With all these circumstances, icebreaker crews are likely to be more familiar than most shipping entering Finnish waters.

Human relations as well as climatic conditions may govern winter trafficking, because icebreakers are civilian, not military vessels. A total crew of approximately 500 serves them. Rather more than half of the crews are recruited seasonally from among seamen living around the south-west coast and archipelagoes. *Karhu*, *Sampo* and *Murtaja* have crews of 58; *Tarmo*, 63; vessels, such as *Voima*, have a complement exceeding 70. Labour relations are important and operations can be brought to a standstill by disagreements.

Today, Finland has seven major icebreakers – *Tarmo*, *Karhu*, *Sampo*, *Apu*, *Voima*, *Murtaja* and *Sisu*. They are the spearheads of its assault upon the frozen Baltic and of its assistance to ice-beleaguered vessels. In number they are the same as before the war; but in effectiveness they are much greater. In energy alone, their collective horsepower is $3\frac{1}{2}$ times that of the pre-war fleet. Until 1950, the units of the icebreaker fleet were mostly attached to individual harbours to which they owed a certain allegiance. Today, they are subject to a unified and central control, and flexibility is the keynote of their manipulation.

Their management and maintenance are taxing partly because of the uncertainty that surrounds their operation. Periods of intense activity are liable to alternate with periods of relative slackness (as can be seen from Figure 16). These variations reflect both physical and economic circumstances.

Life on board an icebreaker is exacting down to the detail of noise, for during a passage through ice-covered seas there is no escape from it. Even in his humble wooden vessel, Edward Clarke likened the noise of the colliding ice floes to 'the sound of a hundred drums beating'. The percussion of ice floe and ice pack reverberating through the steel hull of a modern vessel adds a hundred tympani and a hundred kettle-drums.

For Georges Duhamel, recording his impressions from Finland, it was a part of the exhilaration of a winter crossing [8].

'Je fus, une nuit, réveillé par un fracas prodigieux. Le hublot, grand comme une paume, portait un pélage de givre; mais je parvins à l'ouvrir pour regarder au

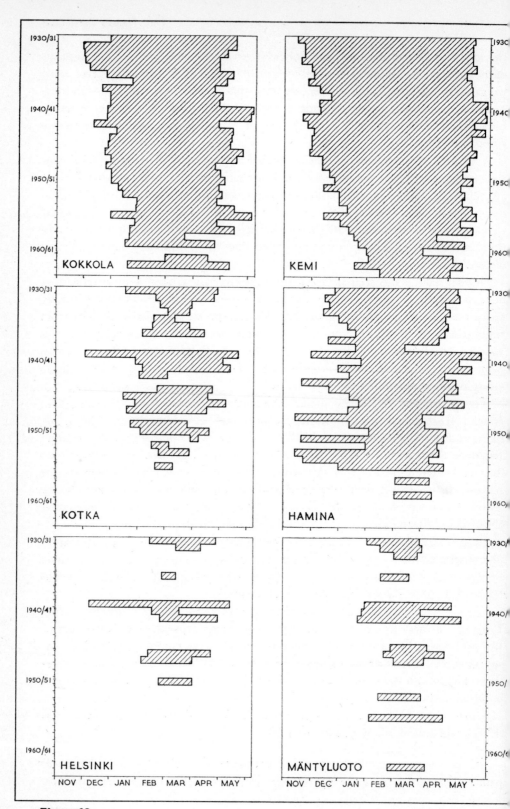

**Figure 18**

dehors. Toute la mer était gêlée. *L'Ukko* fendait la banquise. Le petit cargo courageux pesait de toute son étrave sur l'immense plaque de sucre. Cela produisait un déchirement merveilleux, le bruit – mais géant, mais divin – que fâit le diamant du vitrier mordant la vitre. Les blocs brisés se vousculaient et rebondissaient sur les tôles. Et le bateau, haletant, tremblait de tous son ossature en se frayant un chemin dans cette mer minérale.'

The *fracas* may be entertaining as a solitary experience; but not as a continuous background to living. It is not surprising that on the latest icebreakers, crews' quarters are lifted as high as possible in the superstructure of the ship.

### The Consequences of the Assault on Winter Icing

The assault on winter icing has had four consequences. First, the entire rhythm of trading has been relaxed. Figure 26 illustrates the substantial volume of contemporary winter trading activity in relation to the total annual trading. Rhythms persist, but their oscillations have been greatly reduced. The restoration of trading over the Russian boundary modifies the situation a little. In terms of volume, Finland's foreign trade is double that of the best pre-war years and the need for winter traffic has grown considerably. Secondly, Finland has assembled a remarkable store of knowledge about the behaviour of winter icing in the Baltic Sea. Thirdly, it has acquired an understanding of icebreakers which a conjunction of circumstances has converted into a new industry of national consequence. Fourthly, in overcoming the forces of physical resistance, Finland has entered into new and positive relations with its similarly affected neighbours.

The deployment of icebreakers, which in any case operate for a considerable part of their time outside territorial waters, pays a growing regard to international relations. An international agreement was drawn up in 1961 formalizing the principles of co-operation between Denmark, Norway, Sweden and Finland in the employment of their icebreaker fleets [9]. From the Finnish point of view, the agreement regularises a situation that has long prevailed. Finland's icebreaker fleet has always co-operated closely with that of Sweden. Under normal circumstances, it is their common interest in the Åland and Bothnian Seas which binds them together; while, during more severe winters, they are jointly concerned with keeping open the entrances to the Baltic as well as the sea lanes in it. The movement of *Sampo* to the Öresund to cope with ice obstruction in February 1963 illustrates the geographical extent of co-operation. The latest development at the international level is a Finnish agreement with West Germany. An icebreaker ordered by West Germany from Finland will have a Finnish crew, operate in

**Figure 18. Dates of Departure of Last Ship and of Arrival of First Ship at six Finnish Ports during the Winters from 1930–1 to 1963–4**

It will be observed that the development has been especially pronounced since 1955–6. (Based on information kindly provided by Dr. E. Palosuo of the Marine Research Institute, Helsinki)

Finnish waters under normal circumstances, but be available for use in West German waters as required.

Within the space of a century, wrote Henrik Ramsay twenty years ago, winter trafficking to and from Finland has been transformed from a dream to a reality. Ultimate success in winter trafficking assumes a maximum of national flexibility in the face of inflexible physical conditions. Much remains to be done – the determination of priorities in hard winters, the search for new protected skerry routes (and their canalization), the fuller employment of ice-strengthened vessels (e.g. tankers), the co-ordination of road, rail and port.

## The Use of Ice Thawing Techniques

The earliest method used in Scandinavia for preventing fairways from freezing was probably described by Olaus Magnus in his *History* in 1555. He wrote of the fat of seals being poured on the water 'in great quantity' and being 'dilated and spread about' in order to keep channels open for friendly shipping – or to lay traps for the enemy. Contemporarily, the most widely used methods employ compressed air in order to promote vertical circulation of water. The first experiments in the use of compressed air bubbles for preventing the formation of ice and for melting it were already made in Canada and the U.S.A. before the First World War [10].

The basic principle of the method is to produce a vertical circulation of water so that the surface layers may be prevented from freezing or may be thawed by natural heat stored in the warmer lower layers. The effectiveness of the method depends upon the difference in temperature between surface water layers and deeper water layers, upon the nature of currents in the water, upon the degree of pressure employed and upon the depth from which the compressed air bubbles rise. In Lake Saimaa (Suur-Saimaa), water temperature in midwinter increases from 0·33°C. at 1 m. depth to 0·76°C. at 3 m., 1·11°C. at 5 m. and 1·45°C. at 10 m.

In Finland, the use of compressed air for thawing ice was first seriously investigated during the Second World War. Defensive measures during the Winter War of 1939–40 called for means of hindering tanks in their advance over frozen lakes and rivers. At first, explosives were used to break up ice surfaces and heat was used locally to dissolve them; but already in 1940 the compressed air method was experimentally used at Manamajärvi, near Oulu. Investigations on Manama lake confirmed that water temperatures were already above freezing point at a depth of 1 m. even in hard winters. During Finland's Continuation War (1941–44), compressed air methods were widely investigated and experiments in many different areas demonstrated their effectiveness. It was not long after the war before the significance of ice-thawing techniques was observed by industry and transport.

Icing normally interrupts the smooth flow of raw materials which feed the softwood mills. Thus, the basins in which Finland's pulpwood and saw logs are stored freeze for five or six months of the year. In former times, it was the common practice to stock-pile logs on land against the period of the winter freeze. Today storage basins are usually employed and they are kept free of ice by different methods. Air compressors, with distributors leading to perforated plastic pipes, are an integral part of the equipment of most large saw mill and pulp mill basins throughout Finland. They were already being employed at Korpilahti on Lake Päijänne in 1949. By the early 1950's, Enso Gutzeit had installed an apparatus at its Saimaa plants. Today, its Kaukopää mill on the south shore of Lake Saimaa keeps a storage basin of 100 ha. free by the use of air compressors and a network of pipes. In general, large plants use a combination of several ice prevention methods. The most direct method is to use waste heat (especially hot water) from the processing plant; but this can only be employed for very limited areas and may not be adequate to maintain an ice-free basin under the hard conditions that prevail, for example, at Veitsiluoto or Kemijärvi in north Finland. A third form of assistance used to combat ice in timber storage basins is the so-called surface current generator. This equipment is used to release log bundles from ice and to open channels for them to the main ice-free basin.

Transport in the Lake District is considerably disturbed by winter icing. Compressed air mechanisms are consequently employed to assist many of Finland's 124 inland ferries. Depending on the location and character of individual ferry routes, air compressors are used in one of several ways – to keep a waterway open throughout the winter, to keep open a route until such time as a safe winter road may replace the ferry route over the lake or river, to hasten the opening of ferry routes during the spring thaw. The services of air compressors are also employed to melt ice in already frozen channels. The degree of their effectiveness is such that, given a stream of 30,000–40,000 litres of compressed air per minute, an ice layer of 80 cm. can be dissolved in two days.

Most of the schemes used for keeping open storage basins are tailor-made to suit the needs of particular enterprises. As in other areas of winter activity, the demand for them or for the components to construct them, has also given rise to a minor producing industry in its own right.

Ice thawing techniques have a short history in Finland. They are based upon simple physical principles and are unspectacular, but they are used increasingly widely and with increasing ingenuity. Although they are one of the lesser forms of assault on the winter freeze, they are a most important auxiliary in the equipment of some of Finland's largest industrial plants and oldest-established highway routes.

## (b) THE OBSTRUCTION OF SNOW

### Snow and National Communications

Figure 4 gives some idea of snowfall conditions for Finland at large. By Norwegian standards, the volume of snow is modest. Indeed, snow deficiency is as likely to raise difficulties as snow surfeit. The criterion of a 'good winter' for the forester is a winter with ample snowfall on solidly frozen ground. The hydro-electric engineer, for whom an adequate level in lake reservoirs is largely dependent upon winter snow, is equally concerned with its volume.

Yet snow raises obstacles where rain does not. Save for the minority who use the sleigh, it interferes with communications. Snow is an obstruction to highway authorities, to railroad operators and to airport authorities, For each authority, the surface area of track increases annually and the tasks of clearance and of maintenance mount correspondingly. The task reaches its climax in urban areas, above all in Helsinki.

There are approximately 70,000 km. of public highways in Finland, 40,000 of them are maintained by the central road authority and the rest by local authorities (who receive a large measure of financial support from the central government). In addition, there are 150,000 km. of private roads, most of which are the responsibility of forestry organizations, private companies and farmers. The length of highways cleared of snow multiplied tenfold in the period 1954–64. In recent winters, snow ploughs have driven well over 6 million km. annually in their clearance operations [11].

The winter programme of road maintenance is a response to snowfall and to low temperatures in juxtaposition. It calls for the clearance of snow, the prevention of snow accumulation, the winter maintenance of road surfaces, the preparation of a limited number of winter roads and the organization of winter ferry routes.

Clearing the obstruction of snow is a national operation. The most common type of snow plough used in Finland is the lorry plough. It is a formidable vehicle with a front plough about 3 m. broad. Its logical ancestor was the device observed by de Capell Brooke in the 1820's – a triangular structure 'which might be pushed forward by two oxen'. The central road authority possesses about 1,600 snow ploughs and a fleet of 700 lorries to drive them. In addition, it hires some 800 private lorries. A high ploughing speed (50–60 km. per hour) enables the fleet to cover the maximum amount of highway as soon as snow begins to fall. At the same time, it enables the snow to be thrown sufficiently far from the edge of the road to prevent the building-up of 'snow walls'. Tractor ploughs are more commonly used on private roads.

The volume of snow varies regionally, but it is almost always greater in the northern third (cf. Figure 5). The intensity of traffic to be served is always greater in the southern third of the country. These two facts guide the distribution and employment of snow removal equipment.

Snow accumulation on highways is partly reduced by the use of snow fences. About 3,500 km. of them are used in Finland and they are largely concentrated in the northern third. They are especially needed in open country where by breaking the wind speed, they prevent deep drifts from accumulating across the road surface. In Lapland, they are frequently permanent structures and may be several metres high. Elsewhere, they are more commonly removed and stored at road sides in summer.

Given facilities for snow clearance and the prevention of snow accumulation, the satisfactory maintenance of road surfaces in winter calls for equally great energies. Again, the problem is exaggerated in the south, because of the risk of temperatures rising to 0°C. or above and because of the intensity of traffic. Traffic speedily compacts fallen snow and transforms it into an uneven, icy surface. Grading machines, provided with indented blades, are the antidote to these conditions [12]. In a normal winter grading machines drive 1·5 million km. in order to break up icy road surfaces. At the same time, sanding is widely practised to reduce accidents on icy roads. Sand heaps, hoppers, silos and even tower silos are multiplying along Finnish highways in order to fight the battle against slipperiness. The largest amount of sand is distributed in the three south-westernmost provinces – nearly half of the total weight used. 'Water sanding' is practised in north Finland, where sub-zero temperatures can be guaranteed. If sand is 'fixed' on the road surface by a fine spray of water, it may be effective for several days. Salt and Calcium chloride are also used in the south to keep road surfaces clear, but they give rise to considerable corrosion problems. The total cost of sanding winter highways is greater than the total cost of clearing them by snow plough, despite the fact that the sand-treated distance is only a quarter of the snow ploughed distance.

A limited number of true winter roads – about 1,100 km. in all – are ploughed across the frozen surfaces of bays and lakes. About 900 km. of them are intended for horse-drawn vehicles only. They provide short cuts across the intricate inlets along the Bothnian coast, release the archipelagoes of Lake Saimaa from their summer detachment and provide links (as in the coastal archipelagoes around Helsinki) for cars to visit island cottages. In the exceptional winter of 1965–6, a 'private' road was opened across the Quarken from Björkö in Finland to Umeå in Sweden. A charge of 10 Finnish marks per automobile and 2 marks per passenger was made for its use. These winter roads are additional to the special roads opened by forestry organizations and by private individuals, which are far more extensive.

The obstruction of snow is experienced on the railway as well as on the road. The problem is most acute for the limited network of north Finnish lines – especially between Oulu, Kemi and Kemijärvi; but the volume of snow encountered is rarely as heavy as on the railways of neighbouring Norway and Sweden. Four major snow ploughs, each generating its own energy and using rotary propellors for snow removal, operate in North Finland. Normal snowfall is dealt with by 92 large-sized snow ploughs and 97 ploughs used in association with the widely-employed diesel cars. These move around the country as required. The larger stations and goods-yards are equipped with ice-removal machines, of which there is a stock of 18. From the beginning, most of this snow and ice-clearing equipment has been manufactured in Finland. The earliest models have an honourable place among the relics in the railway museum. Contemporary equipment is constructed principally in the railway workshops of Tampere.

## Snow in an Urban Context

Snow clearance and highway maintenance are most critical in urban areas. As in all modern cities with elaborate transport nets and a large number of private cars, the communications of a city such as Helsinki are expected to operate with equal efficiency at all times of the year. Snow disposal problems in Helsinki differ in form rather than degree from those of Oslo or Stockholm; while the scale of operations is less than in the far larger cities of Leningrad or Moscow.

City responsibility for street clearance was slow to emerge. Even after the coming of the internal combustion engine, much Helsinki street traffic continued to change from wheel to runner in winter. The sleigh and 'spark' have only quitted the city streets in the last generation. Two generations ago, snow obstruction regularly hampered city movement. A children's game from the 1890's, *Omnibus spel*, contains a rhyming couplet for Helsinki which runs

> Nu möts af snö, ett hinder
> Som dig här på platsen binder
> *(Står över ett kast)*

> (Now we meet snow, a hindrance
> which confines you to your place.
> Forego one throw.)

In the winter of 1964–5, some 600 km. of city roads, streets and squares called for attention. Expressed in surface area, this meant over 8 sq. km. In addition, an area five times as big was cleared privately. Extensive roof clearance in the centre of the city (undertaken by janitors frequently tethered to chimney stacks) adds to the burden of snow clearance.

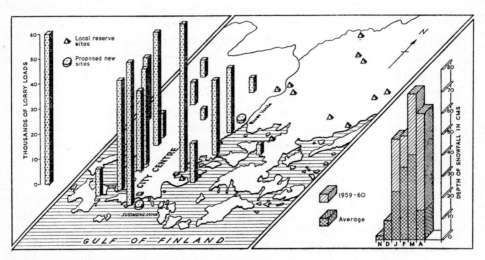

**Figure 19. Snowfall and Snow Removal in Helsinki for the Winter 1961–2**
(Based on *Lumenkaatopaikkakomitean mietintö*, Helsinki, 1965)

The volume of snow to be removed varies appreciably from year to year. It depends upon freeze and thaw conditions during the winter, as well as upon the actual snowfall. Monthly snowfall is also very capricious. In the winter of 1959–60 for example, a greater volume of snow had to be cleared in April than in January or February. The absolute volume of snow to be removed averages about 3·5 million cu. m.; but, in 1959–60 (see Figure 19), it rose to 6 million cu. m. In terms of transport, this amounts to approximately 500,000 lorry loads. In the winter of 1961–2 (see Figure 19), when a detailed examination of the operation was undertaken, the figure was 458,000 loads.

The city of Helsinki has 100 snow ploughs; but others may be hired if needed. Snow removal requires careful planning. Both the city and private property owners hire lorries and tractors with trucks for snow removal. An average lorry load amounts to about 7 cu. m. of snow. Vehicles are hired on permanent contract and farmers around the city may also provide them. The largest lorry contracting firms may muster several hundred lorries – and they may contract to work by night after having fulfilled other functions by day.

The maximum convenient distance for transport is 3–5 km. Around Helsinki, there are 21 major snow dumps. Their location (together with additional proposed sites) is shown on Figure 19. Most of these snow dumps are on the ice immediately adjacent to the peninsula. The peninsularity of Helsinki offers distinct advantages for snow disposal. But the availability of dumping sites is very restricted; because, except for a limited period in harder winters, it is hazardous for heavily laden lorries to cross sea ice. Snow dumps are regarded as unsightly, especially during the melting period – and they may not disappear until early summer. Some idea of the magnitude of these snow dumps is provided by Plate 11. Needless to say, there is an additional local problem in the solid residue left behind. It is estimated that every lorry load of snow yields an accumulation of 2·5–3·00 mm. of solid matter.

The alternative to removal is melting *in situ*. The employment of wood-burning snow-melters forty years ago is echoed in contemporary experimental devices. Helsinki is the first city in Europe to have tried out an American snow-melting machine. Such tractor-drawn machines, capable of dissolving 40 tons an hour, dispose of snow more cheaply than lorry transport, but there are many mechanical defects to overcome: snow-melting machines are also used to hasten the clearance of sports grounds. Under-pavement or under-highway heating are little used in Finland; but Helsinki airport, in addition to employing rotary-type snow blowers, is also kept free of snow by heaters beneath much of the runway. Off-peak electrical current is also used to speed snow melting at certain dumping sites.

The task of snow removal grows as the suburbs proliferate and extend over greater distances. It becomes increasingly complicated as the traffic of the city intensifies and parking makes greater demands on the limited area of cleared surface. Helsinki has a special snow clearance committee to deal with the difficulties. Its deliberations revolve around the multiplication and more effective use of snow dumps, coupled with fleets of lorry ploughs, trucks, tractor brushes and sidewalk ploughs. The search for suitable disposal sites is a problem in planning, which must constantly balance economy against amenity. One physical fact which affects snow dumps is that the inner Baltic is virtually tideless, so that the waters around Helsinki have no cleansing tidal scour. Nevertheless, a pontoon bridge is proposed between the south-end of Helsinki peninsula and a snow dump on offshore Sirpalesaari, the coast of which is at least subject to vigorous wave-action during open water.

### The Problem of the Thaw

The worst effects of winter occur at the end of the season and bring to a climax the difficulties of overland movement. It is the time of *kelirikko* (Sw. *tjällossning*), and it lasts 4–6 weeks. Figure 20 indicates its duration, though the peak impact will occur at different times in different parts of the country. The thaw, disturbing the surface of the ground by both meltwater run-off and frost release, has traditionally brought sleighing to an end and its effects seriously disturb wheeled traffic. The degree of disturbance is greatest when the thaw is rapid or when it is accompanied by rain.

The problem is rooted in the type of soil. The extent to which frost penetrates is an expression of the character of the soil as well as of the intensity of the cold. The size of soil particles and the amount of soil water held in suspension both affect the degree of penetration, the formation of frost lenses and the nature of soil upheaval with the rise in springtime temperatures. Gravels, sands and peats do not suffer serious frost upheaval in spring. Moraines, clays and silts are subject to considerable disturbance. Figure 8, which shows regional differences in the depth to which the ground freezes, presents the problem for Finland at large.

Frost upheaval has many consequences. The farmer is concerned with its effects on his autumn-sown crops, which may be partly uprooted as the surface of the soil is disturbed and which may be subject to 'stretching' in the diurnal succession of spring-winter frost and thaw. All forms of building construction must pay regard to frost upheaval and the preparation of foundations is the subject of much care (see Figure 25). Road engineers are especially sensitive to the consequences of 'heaving', which have four expressions – massive heaving, layer disturbance, surface disturbance and holes-with-ruts.

Down to the 1950's, most Finnish roads (including the main highways) were 'dirt' roads and maintenance engineers accepted a prolonged springtime disturbance of their surfaces as inevitable. Springtime road conditions for traffic are advised on television programmes, with varying degrees of gloom and glee.

Prevention of frost heaving on roads is largely a matter of construction. In the past, Finland has lacked the finance to construct highways satisfactory for its climatic conditions. The risk of disturbance can be very considerably reduced by deepening road beds to a minimum of 36 cms. A 20 cms. bed of sand supporting 10 cms. of broken stones, 4 cms. of asphalt and a top layer of 2 cms. of fine chips is the remedy which is being employed on most main highways. Finland's asphalt-surfaced highways grew from about 100 km. in the early 1950's to over 10,000 km. a decade later. The asphalt derives principally as a bye-product from oil-refining (in itself an industry closely related to many of the agencies which have reduced Finland's dependence upon winter).

The consequences of improved highway construction have been striking. In 1963, which was an average winter, only 16% of Finland's national highways were affected by the thaw. The percentage of local authority highways affected was 42%. Disturbance began in the middle of April, reached a peak during the first week of May, disappeared on the main highways by mid-June, but lingered on local authority roads in north Finland until mid-July. The average date for the worst *kelirikko* for the country at large is the first week of May.

Figure 20 illustrates the remarkable change brought about by highway improvement schemes in the last fifteen years. It also indicates the fuller understanding of a situation which absence of statistics formerly denied. In 1951, one of the earliest investigations into the effects of the thaw estimated that the roads serving three-quarters of the inhabited area of Finland were seriously disturbed, that the disturbance lasted from 4–6 weeks and that it directly involved the movements and activities of 1½ million people. At that time, it was estimated that the percentage of roads with traffic restrictions was least in the south-west and most in the eastern

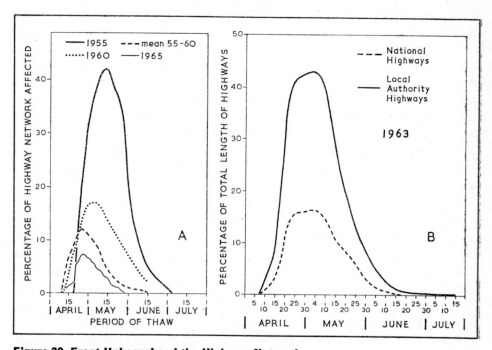

**Figure 20. Frost Upheaval and the Highway Network**

(Diagram A is based on E. Rinne, Winter maintenance of roads in Finland, *Neve*, Torino, 1965; Diagram B is based on *Tie-ja vesirakennukset*, Finland's Official Statistics, XIX, 78, 1964)

interior. The figure rose from 10–15% in the south-west, through 45–50% in Kuopio and Oulu areas to 70% in Kainuu and 88·5% in Mikkeli.

The story told by Figure 20 reflects the same kind of response to the use of new technical facilities as does that told by Figure 18. Winter communications on land have undergone a change no less fundamental than those at sea; but the story is less dramatic.

The thaw also brings problems of meltwater and of ice pressure along the interior waterways. It is a time of hazard for dams and for bridge supports. In order to reduce the threat of widespread flooding, ice packs must be exploded on rivers and at lake narrows. Thus, in 1960, substantial expenditure was required on Vanda, Kokemäki, Merikarvia, Kuivamiemi, Olhava and Yli-Ii rivers; in 1963, it was the Kymi river which required most attention.

## (c) *LIGHT IN THE DARKNESS*

Winter in Finland spells a measure of darkness. The higher the latitude the greater the disturbance in the rhythm of darkness and daylight. In the far north of Finland and to a certain extent in the deep south, the periods of light and darkness are seasonal rather than diurnal for a part of the year. In theory, the different seasonal rhythms of daylight and darkness ought to have some effect upon the periodicity of human activity and behaviour. Be that as it may, darkness is a challenge – at both the physical and the mental levels.

The impact of climate (including daylight and darkness rhythms) upon mentality is a study which has only advanced at a snail's pace since Lord Byron declared 'the cold in clime are cold in blood'. The relationship of sleeping and waking to variations in the alternation of daylight and darkness is a territory which has only experienced marginal investigation by scientists [14]. Sleep rhythms appear to be acquired characteristics, though medical opinion would rule out neither hereditary nor cosmic influences. In high latitudes, the normal daily demand for approximately eight hours of sleep is not automatically extended in winter.

If north Norwegian experiences are anything to go by – and there is no reason to believe that north Finnish experiences are different – the period of sleep in winter only averages an hour more than in summer. The effects of winter darkness and of low temperature conditions on sleeping habits are more indirect than direct. Where darkness and cold are most prolonged, there seem to be psychological reactions; but there is insufficient scientifically collected information to make any formal assessment of the influence. One fact is quite clear – that it is more economical to sleep in the dark period and to work in the light.

Darkness has always been challenged by artificial light. 'The northern peoples, being subject to most long nights use divers kinds of lights so that they may do their necessary offices for their household benefit', observed Olaus Magnus. With the aid of light, they have been able to live much the same as people in other latitudes. The matter has always been most pressing at the domestic level. In historical times, the demand for artificial light was usually met from the forest, though seal or train oil also provided a source of illumination around the coasts. The best inner parts of the pine tree, dried and split down the centre, provided the resinous torches which were used in every home. These were called *päre* (*päreet*, in the plural) in Finnish and *pärtbloss* in Swedish [15]. They were prepared in large numbers for the winter months and they were yet another cause of the early inroads on the best pinewood stands. The torches played a special role at the midwinter solstice and on Christmas day a special *julbloss*, the *julfula* (in Finnish, *joulusoihtu*) was used to illumine the churchyard. Torches were employed on the sledges arriving for the Christmas services. The *päre* was an unsatisfactory means of lighting. It had a low power of illumination, needed frequent replacement and the naked flame was a natural hazard. In richer homes, the *päre* was replaced by tallow candles – 'as long as one's arm, according to the length of the night', in the words of Olaus Magnus.

The oil lamp was slow to make an appearance. Only within the lifetime of men has its soft and steadier light been suffused through the countryside. Indeed, coal gas provided illumination for Helsinki and for Viipuri before oil lamps began to make a common appearance up-country. The introduction of the oil lamp to the countryside is presented both literally and symbolically by Juhani Aho in one of his short stories from Savo. The story, published in 1893, is called 'When Father Bought the Lamp' [16]. The following conversation reflects the attitude of the countryfolk to this new invention.

'Hark ye, mother, ought'n't we to buy a lamp?'
'A lamp? What sort of lamp?'
'What! Don't you know that the storekeeper who lives in the market town has brought from St Petersburg lamps that actually burn better than ten *pärettä*? They've already got a lamp at the parsonage.'
'Oh, yes! Isn't it one of those things which shine in the middle of the room so that we can see to read in every corner, just as if it was broad daylight?'

But the oil lamp alone was insufficient to change terms of reference deriving from a land where night took precedence over day. Zachris Topelius observed that a three day old child in midwinter Finland was a three night old child (*kolme öinen vanha lapsi*).

The oil lamp is still a regularly used supplement in remoter country districts; but electricity is now carried to fully nine-tenths of Finland's homes to provide the essential source of illumination. Electric lighting began to make its appearance in the 1880's. Finlayson's mill in Tampere, which switched on its electric light in the autumn of 1882, was among the first in Europe to employ the new form of lighting. Among the curios of Häme museum in Tampere are some of the original electric light bulbs.

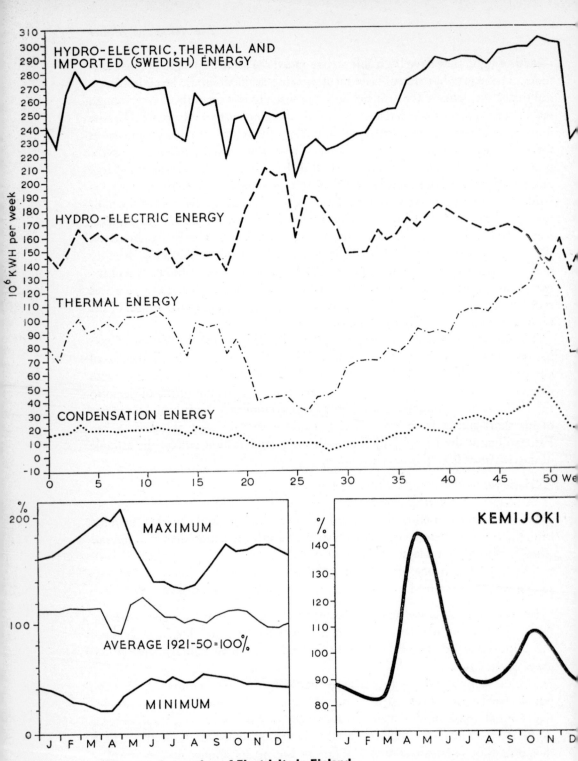

**Figure 21. Generation of Electricity in Finland**

The top graphs indicate data on a weekly basis for 1964. The bottom left hand diagram shows the energy potential of the principal lake systems. (Source: *Suomen Sähkölaitosyhdistys.*) The bottom right hand diagram illustrates the monthly variation in water volume of the Kemi river.

80

7. March in North Finland, with embossed snow on spruce trees.

8

9

8. *Voima*, one of Finland's larger icebreakers, on patrol.
9. An ice hole fisherman (Pilkkijä), outside Helsinki. The 'corkscrew' is for boring the ice hole.
10. A boy in a blizzard in front of the University Library, Helsinki. Wind is a winter factor to be contended with.

11. One of the 60,000 lorry loads of snow which must be deposited in Helsinki bay in an average winter.

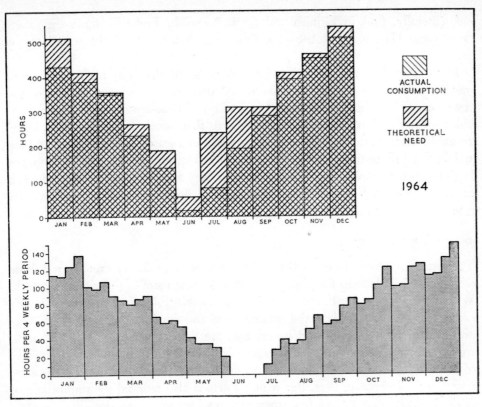

**Figure 22. City Lights**

The upper graph shows the theoretical need and actual consumption of electricity used to light the streets of Helsinki in 1964. The lower graph illustrates the weekly consumption.
(Based on information supplied by the Helsinki City Electricity Authority)

The need for artificial illumination is a consequence of the rhythms of daylight and darkness shown in Figure 22. In the rural sector of the economy, the routine has changed with the years; but the number of hours when artificial light is required for farm work changes little. One of the first statements on the subject was printed in a farmers' journal in 1849 [17]. For southern Finland it estimated an annual total of 1,319 hours; with a need in January and December of eight hours daily – four in the morning and four in the evening. In urban districts, public lighting is added to private lighting. Figure 22 shows the weekly demand for lighting in the streets in Helsinki for 1964. It also indicates the theoretical and actual hours needed on a monthly basis. The divergence is a consequence of cloud conditions.

In contrast to the illumination of Finnish towns and cities, which are lit with an extravagance that outshines those of most countries, are the solitary but critical beacons which flash around Finland's intricate and islanded coast. Its original lighthouses were flaming beacons, as indicated by the use of the words *palo* (literally, fire) in Finnish and *fyr* in Swedish. Finland's most significant beacon was Hangö lighthouse – the first to flash throughout the round of the year.

In summer, beacons are unnecessary because of the light nights and, contrastingly, they are not required over extended areas in winter because of the cessation of shipping. The annual 'List of Lights' (*Suomen rannikon loistot*) provided for navigation in Finnish waters records that, south of latitude 62°N, lights are exhibited from the beginning of the navigational season in spring until 15 June and from 1 July until the end of the navigational season; north of 62°N, from the beginning of the navigational season until 25 May and from 20 July until the end of the navigational season. Many more coastal lights are used throughout the round of the year than was formerly the case; but plenty are still extinguished.

## Breaking Winter's Siege

The assault on winter has something of the nature of a military exercise and those who mount it adhere to the philosophy that the best form of defence is to attack. Within living memory, Finland has made a considerable effort to break winter's siege. The effort proceeds at the national level and the domestic level; it has features which are publicised and others that are disregarded. The frontal attack, conducted at the national level, is expressed in terms of millions of horsepower of mechanical energy on land and no less than 143,000 horsepower is concentrated in the icebreaker fleet. But winter's grip is also reduced by a multitude of devices which affect only a few square metres here and a few hundred hectares elsewhere. The hand-operated snow ploughs, for example, which clear the sidewalks of suburbs help to remove a winter obstacle no less than the simple but highly effective pressure pipes that prevent ice accumulation in the log harbours of softwood plants. Meanwhile, winterization of motor vehicles is so completely accepted that it is disregarded and drivers turn automatically to the studded winter tyre as their grandfathers to the ruffled winter horseshoes.

The cumulative effect of all these innovations is that Finland is able to relax just a little more each time winter sounds its annual imperatives. If not exactly raising a battle cry, Finns are increasingly emboldened to exclaim, 'Bore, beware.'

## BIBLIOGRAPHY

[1] L. W. Fagerlund, *op. cit.*, p. 43.

[2] K. W. Palmén, Om isbrytar-ångfartyg och vintersjötrafik, *Tekniska Föreningens i Finland Förhandlingar*, Helsingfors, 1894.

[3] The full story of the icebreaker is told down to 1946 in H. Ramsay, *I Kamp med Östersjöns isar*, Helsingfors, 1947. Parts of this section are based on Ramsay's account.

[4] From *Dikter i Väntan*, Helsingfors, 1890.

[5] *Suomen asetuskokoelma*, 1960, 163. The tax is subject to periodic revision.

[6] The two following sections are based upon discussions with Dr. J. E. Jansson, whose kind assistance is deeply appreciated. Reference has also been made to J. E. Jansson, Icebreakers and their design, *European Shipbuilding*, 1956, 5, 1–27; C. Landtman, Technische Gesichtspunkte über moderne grosse Eisbrecher, *Jahrbuch der Schiffbautechnischen Gesellschaft*, 1961, 55, 142–74; *Svensk Sjöfartstidning*, 1964, 7.

[7] E. Palosuo, *A Treatise on Severe Ice Conditions, op. cit.* and personal communications.

[8] G. Duhamel, *Géographie cordiale de l'Europe*, Paris, 1931, p. 246.

[9] *Suomen sopimukset*, 1961, 36.

[10] P. Kaitera, Jääpeitteen sulattamisesta paineilmaa ja veden lämpövaroja hyväksikäyttäen, *Teknillinen aikakauslehti*, 1946, 5, 1–10, and T. Liukko, Jäättömät vesiväylät Suomessa, *Tehostaja*, 1957, 9; Jääpeitteen sulattaminen vesistön omilla lämpövaroilla, *Rakennus Insinööri*, 1947, 6.

[11] *Tie ja vesirakennukset, Finland's Official Statistics*, XIX, 78, 1964.

[12] E. Rinne, Winter maintenance of roads in Finland, *Neve*, Torino, 1965, 7 and O. Taivainen, Two decades of development of winter clearance techniques in Finland, *Tielehti*, 1965, 7, 8.

[13] H. Saarento, Experience of mechanical snow melting in Helsinki, *Tielehti*, 1965, 8.

[14] cf. K. Kjos, Sleep disturbance as a school hygiene problem in north Norway, *Tskr. Norske Laege Forening*, Oslo, 78, 1958; N. Kleitman, *Sleep and Wakefulness*, Chicago, 1963, and H. W. Lewis and I. P. Masterman, Sleep and Wakefulness in the Arctic, *Lancet*, I, 1957, 1262–6.

[15] G. Grotenfelt, Om pärtbloss . . . och dyl., *Meddelanden från Statens Agriculturethnografiska Samlingar à Mustiala Institut*, Helsingfors, 1920, 141–2.

[16] R. Nisbet Bain (tr.), J. Aho, *Squire Hellman and Other Stories*, London, 1893. In the original the story has the title, *Siihen aikaan, kun isä lampun osti*.

[17] *Tidning för Landtbrukare och Näringsidkare*, Åbo, 1849, 39.

The instinct of men and animals in seeking refuge from the winter is that of survival. Survival in a cold environment gives rise to a variety of adaptations. These aim at conservation or creation of heat. Among animals, extremes of adaptation are found in migration and hibernation. In cold environments, men construct shelters for themselves and for their domestic stock in which artificial climates are created. Clothing similarly creates an artificial micro-climate around the body. The luxuries of other lands, such as central heating or fur coats, become the necessities of winter existence in a country such as Finland. In former times, eating and drinking habits also differed in winter and summer; but, with methods of conservation and new means of communication, significant seasonal changes in diet have been largely eliminated.

Refuge from winter implies the creation of a whole series of buffers between man and low temperatures. The motive is the same today as in primitive times, but the range of manoeuvrability is far greater. There is no ultimate escape from the annual advance of the 'ice age'; but the possibilities of physical protection from it have now reached such a stage that men not only have energy left over to mount assault upon it, but also the urge to play as well as to work with it.

The scientific age which has made this possible expresses heat and light in its own terms. Therefore, such measurements as the calorie have been devised; while engineers have invented kilocalories (1 kilocalorie equals 1,000 calories) in which to express larger quantities of heat. Clothing, too, is reduced to units of bodily insulation, such as the *clo* (which is equated with the weight of indoor clothing worn by an ordinary sedentary worker). These varied units are indispensable for expressing precisely the effects of various forms of protection which men have devised to cushion themselves from cold [1].

## Migration and Hibernation

Fauna react to the descent of winter either by escaping from it or by adapting physiologically to cope with its consequences. For animals and birds, the most important fact about winter is the low temperature which restricts feeding opportunities and consequently affects calorie intake. The fauna of high latitudes has a pronounced seasonal food cycle, in which an abundant and varied summer diet is transformed into a scanty and monotonous winter diet. In the northern winter all birds and most mammals are reduced to consuming the dry seeds, fruits and vegetative parts of trees and shrubs. In a country such as Finland, the pressure upon plants is naturally heavier in the north where the length of the winter season is longest. At the same time, vegetative regeneration is slower in the north than in the south. The length of the day is also a significant feature of winter in faunal behaviour. Eating habits are a natural response to rhythms of daylight and darkness.

Refuge from winter takes several forms. One form of evading winter is to leave it behind. Finland's bird population contains a large proportion of migrants [2]. The dates of their arrival and departure have been long observed by naturalists. Long-distance migrants range from the honey buzzard and osprey to the swifts and swallows. Shorter distance migrants include familiar west European birds such as the blackbird and the curlew, literally blowing in on the warm cyclonic winds that bring the first rains of spring. Within Finland itself, there are also regional migrations in response to winter. Shifts from north to south generally reflect the severity of individual winters. Seabirds, in search of fish, migrate to open waters in winter and return to their coastal nesting places in spring. The mechanism behind migration remains largely a mystery, though rhythms of daylight and darkness, and changes in air pressure probably play roles no less than temperature.

Hibernation is a second form of escape from the effects of winter [3]. It would seem to be a response to a combination of temperature and light conditions as well as degree of food availability. Another way of looking at hibernation is to regard it as a means of heat regulation; though there is one school of thought that regards hibernation as an abnormal form of lethargy, not true sleep, and does not consider that it is necessarily related to low temperatures. There is also evidence to suggest that warm-blooded animals which hibernate have a lower average body temperature than those which do not hibernate. The conditions of darkness associated with hibernation are also partly created by the animals themselves. Burrows and lairs, sometimes calling for elaborate preparation, are retreats from daylight.

The physiological adjustments shown by hibernating mammals are a common slackening of the pulse rate, diminution of blood circulation, reduction in nervous reaction and loss of weight. Changes in metabolism also occur, for example, blood sugar is modified. Detailed studies of the hedgehog (*Erinaceus europaeus*) in

Finland suggest that it may attempt to resist the onset of winter sleep and that hibernation is broken by periodic arousals. The heart rate slows from a summer figure of 210 per minute to a midwinter count of 2–12 per minute; while the blood sugar varies from summer to winter by as much as 60 per cent. The period of hypothermia, with its brief interruptions, may last for 170 days or more [4].

The bear (*Ursus arctos*) has not been subjected to artificially induced sleep in the same laboratory manner as the hedgehog. It is not a true hibernator, but its winter lethargy means that it is usually only a predator for a part of the year. Killings, which have been more scientifically observed in recent years, show a pronounced concentration in May, at the end of the period of sleep, when dens can be most easily sought out and destroyed. The bear has one of the most effective furs possessed by any animal for thermal insulation.

A third form of winter adjustment is shown by some birds [5]. The capercaillie (*Tetrao urogallus*), for example, changes its habitat in winter. During the autumn it joins forces with other birds and leaves the ground for trees. It remains in small flocks until the snow disappears and it is able to feed on the ground again. The black grouse (*Lyrurus tetrix*) similarly takes to arboreal feeding. In both instances, the practice may be partly related to precaution against attack from predatory animals.

Adaptation to snow is shown in a variety of ways. The hazel grouse (*Tetrastes bonasia*), which is subject to prey by the hawk, may bury itself in the snow in the daytime for protection. The willow grouse (*Lagopus lagopus*) and the ptarmigan (*Lagopus mutus*) have feet with 'snow shoe' extensions which enable them to move over softer snow. Other birds must await the hardening of the snow surface before they can move over it. The winter flocking and arboreal feeding of the capercaillie and black grouse is partly related to their difficulty in moving over soft snow.

The depth of snow accumulation and the form of its springtime thaw can seriously affect the breeding habits of birds that winter in Finland. Partridges (*Perdrix perdrix*) provide an example. The date at which bare patches develop in the snow, around hummocks, stumps, and tree trunks or along the banks of streams and ditches, is critical for the provision of early green fodder.

Winter availability of food is not equally critical for all birds. For some, the severity of the winter is the critical fact in the amount of food consumed. For others, it is the amount of food available at the mating season which determines the resistance of the species.

The winter behaviour of herbivors varies greatly. Again, adjustments are highly individual. The elk (*Alces alces*) is an omnivorous twig eater and its liking for bark is sufficient for it to cause substantial damage to trees. Lesser fauna such as the snow hare (*Lepus timidus*) and the field hare (*Lepus europaeus*) turn to aspen, willow and birch twigs – and blueberry shoots until the snow depth exceeds about 20 cms. The field hare, lacking 'snow shoe' features on its hind legs, is not well adjusted to move over soft snow. It has correspondingly greater difficulty in obtaining nourishment and is an easier prey for marauding creatures. The squirrel (*Sciurus vulgaris*) is principal among the lesser herbivors. Its winter food consists principally of spruce seeds, pine seeds or, if they are not available, spruce buds. For this reason, it is a natural enemy of the forester.

The chief browsing animal and the most well known is the reindeer. Reindeer, both wild and domesticated, usually migrate in search of fodder; though the distances which they travel depend on the nature of herding practices. For example, there are Lapps around Lake Inari who have small herds of twenty or thirty animals which only move into the neighbouring forests and do not engage in the longer treks commonly associated with reindeer herding. The reindeer is well adapted to cope with the extended winter of high latitudes: summer is its real problem, with insect pests as the principal difficulty. The reindeer has long been the object of scientific curiosity. Its behaviour was recorded by Johannes Schefferus nearly three hundred years ago [6] and described in Carl Linnaeus' classical *Journey to Lapland* of 1735 [7]. In Finland, where reindeer probably number 150,000, a limited amount of transhumance still takes place at the end of April; but it cannot compare with the situation in Norway and Sweden. Winter is commonly spent in the woodland environment and summer in the fells. Migration offers no prospect of escape from the winter; but it does offer supplementary sources of food supply and also a measure of protection. In general, snow depths in the woodland exceed that of the open fell, but winter food is there more easily obtained as the icerind (*hanki*) is lacking and weakly developed. During winter, reindeer live mostly on reindeer 'mosses' (*Cladonia rangiferina* and *Cladonia alpestris*). These must be obtained from beneath the snow, which the reindeer removes with its hooves. If the ground lichens are in short supply or are inaccessible because of snow, it will turn to the bearded lichens (*Alectoria* and *Usnea*), which grow on the trunks and branches of trees. It will also consume crusted lichens (*Parmelia spp.*).

Immediately dependent on the herbivors are the carnivors. Except for the bear, predatory beasts are more destructive in the winter months than at other times of the year. North-east Finland is still invaded by wolves (*Canis lupus*) during winter, though the boundaries of their distribution have changed swiftly during the last three generations. The wolf is protected by one of the finest insulating furs of any animal (one reason, perhaps, why its skin has formerly been highly esteemed for winter apparel) [8]. Wolf packs (more than eight or nine per pack is unusual in Finland) usually form in autumn and move in north of the pinewood border. They may travel up to 200 km. in a day over the snow on the open fell, but not more than 25 km. in forested country. They prey upon anything from voles and lemmings to capercaillie and reindeer. On firm ground, they can move more quickly than any other Finnish animal; but soft snow impedes them. Packs commonly break up following courtship fights in February and March. Winter invasion of wolves has increased considerably in the south-east since 1944. Wolf hunting had been a regular winter feature in Finland in former times. Today, it is rare, but almost every winter one or two couples are hunted down in south Finland. It may reach a rare technical refinement on the fells where aircraft may be employed to track down the marauders. Other predators that continue to operate during the winter are the lynx (*Lynx lynx*) and the wolverine (*Gulo gulo*); they prey principally on reindeer. The polecat, fox, mink and stoat are minor predators.

## Designs for Living

Finns have always had abundant timber for building and for fuel. Because men and domesticated beasts retreat to house and barn for the greater part of the year, rural buildings tend to be of corresponding amplitude. Formerly, for reasons of security against fire, farm buildings in most parts of Finland tended to be dispersed. When a new farm was established (and the same applied to most of the new holdings created after the second world war), pioneers first built the *sauna* and then the stable. The former housed the family until such time as a proper house could be built. A stable has always been a matter of urgency for new homesteaders, because stock must be kept indoors for six months in south Finland and eight in the north of the country. The stable represents the principal capital investment on most Finnish farms. It is a combined grange and byre, housing the entire stock, together with fodder and implements. It is often a multi-storied unit, the top storey for fodder, the lowest level sometimes arranged for the collection of manure. Stables are usually kept sufficiently warm by natural animal heat, though a measure of central heating may be employed for the piggery. In severe winters, such as 1965–6, the silage pit may freeze and frost invade the root stores, milk production may decline and stock lose weight. One feature of the farm complex that calls for heat is the drying shed. Because of the short growing season, it is frequently necessary to harvest grain before it is thoroughly dried. The old-fashioned *riihi* (Sw. *ria*) has been slowly replaced by new hot-air drying machines.

Given new building materials, e.g. cheap glass and metals, builders have modified their designs accordingly. Architects and constructional engineers pay especially close attention to light factors. In high latitudes, the angle of the sun's rays differs from that in lower latitudes. The extent of window space has grown greatly in recent decades. It reflects the demand for daylight, but also presumes additional heating and/or insulation costs [9].

At the same time, the changing values set upon Finland's forest resources have called for special types of winter accommodation. The lumberjack's camp is a distinctive expression of its latitude. Winter logging camps (*talvikämpät*) are found all over Finland, but mostly in isolated areas away from the established farming communities. In many places, the distance to the working site in the forest is too long to be covered every morning and evening, the more so because winter days are short. In the southern half of Finland, the thinly-settled areas lie along the eastern frontier and on the Suomenselkä watershed; in the northern half, they are found in the broad interfluves, the *Kairat*, between the narrow zones of settlement that line the river banks. In all, the winter camps consist of some 4,000

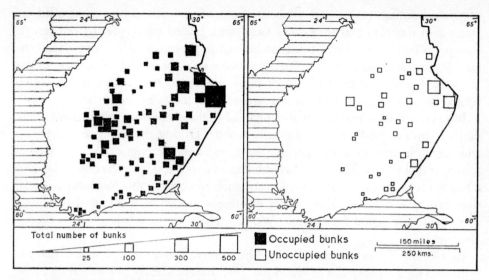

**Figure 23. Loggers Camps belonging to Forest Companies in South Finland, Winter 1964–5**

The maps indicate the declining demand for accommodation resulting from the mechanisation of the logging industry. (Based on information in *Metsäkämppäkomitean mietintö,* 1966)

dwelling units, of which 800 are transportable, and some 1,500 caravan units. They provide accommodation for about 44,000 timber men. The camps have shelters for mechanical equipment.

## The Problem of Heating

Finland's winter heat budget was originally derived principally from wood fuel. Wood fuel still plays a significant part, because Finland has neither coal nor oil. Regardless of considerations of thermal efficiency, sources of fuel supply alternative to wood are of increasing concern. The method of employing domestic fuel continue to vary from the economical to the extravagant; but the methods of heat conservation are increasingly ingenious. Save for a few buildings preserved in open-air museums, the primitive Finnish *savupirtti* (which was still widely encountered a century ago) has disappeared. With its open fire in the centre of the living room and a smoke hole in the roof, it represented a method of heating at once uneconomic and unhealthy. Stone, brick and clay stoves – elaborate in their regional diversity – became dominant features of the living room (F. *tupa* or *pirtti*). They remain so and are often structures a hundred cubic feet or more in size, retentive of heat which they slowly diffuse for several hours after their logs and twigs cease to burn [10]. Country proverbs attest to the winter practice of sleeping on top of the stove. K. A. Tavastjerna has a character, Antti Metsäntausta in his novel *Kapten Törnberg* (1894), whose stove fills a third of the living room and on which he appears to have lain most of the midwinter mornings.

The nineteenth century saw the diffusion throughout Finland of a great variety of wood-burning stoves and kitchen ranges. Tall brick stoves, controlled by systems of dampers and frequently faced with glazed tiles, spread from central Europe to become the usual forms of heating apparatus in other rooms than the kitchen. Edward Clarke made reference to them in his hotel in Turku in the winter of 1800. There have been plenty of rural and urban refinements to these two related pieces of apparatus. Cast iron stoves have partly replaced them.

In 1951, it was estimated that about half of Finland's heating requirements were derived from domestic fuel (principally wood). During the war years, 1939–44, and the immediate post-war period, the woodlands were an even more critical source of fuel supply. The transport of billets of fire-wood to urban centres became a major national enterprise – and forests suffered considerable local and regional overcutting as a result. Many town dwellings as well as most rural dwellings continue to use wood for heating. Wooden chips, derived from mill waste, are also burned.

As a result of this situation, Finland has undertaken a succession of investigations into the consumption of wood fuel [11]. Independently of the heating issue, the subject is of concern for assessing timber replacement and the use of working time. An enquiry into the amount of wood required for heating farmhouses in 1960 has been conducted by M. Honkanen [12]. The amount of wood consumed depends upon the size of the unit of space heated and upon regional variations in the intensity and duration of winter. For buildings up to 150 cu. m. in size, the amount of wood consumed varies from 2·48 in south Finland to 3·47 cu. m. in north Finland: for space up to 600 cu. m., the figures rose to 3·70 and 4·17 cu. m. respectively. Honkanen's enquiry also shows that the amount of time spent on felling, sawing, splitting and transporting the billets of firewood, varies from 1·6 to 4·7 per cent of the total time devoted to farm work. Again, the lower figure was for smaller buildings in the south and the higher figure for larger buildings in the north. In addition, the maintenance of log fires is estimated to occupy at least 7 per cent of the working time of the housewife.

The import of fuel for heating and energy engages the growing attention of Finland. The first significant substitutes for wood were coal and coke – coke, being in part a by-product of the domestic gas plants which were already established in Helsinki and Viipuri over a century ago. To coal and coke were recently added oil. In 1951, the fuel demands of Finland were the equivalent of 10 million tons of steam coal and imported fuels accounted for about 30 per cent of this figure. In 1957, the demand was 13·8 million tons, with import figures up to 37 per cent [13]. In 1965 energy demand exceeded 20·0 million tons. (Coal and coke 16%, oil 35%, wood fuel and peat, etc. 27%, water power 22%.) The dependence on imported sources of supply exceeded 40 per cent. As in the rest of Scandinavia, the rising demand for oil fuels has been dramatic. In response to it and to the associated economies, Finland has two state-operated oil-refining plants, one at Naantali, near Turku and one in Sköldvik, near Helsinki. The use of oil fuel has transformed Finland's ability to deal with winter problems.

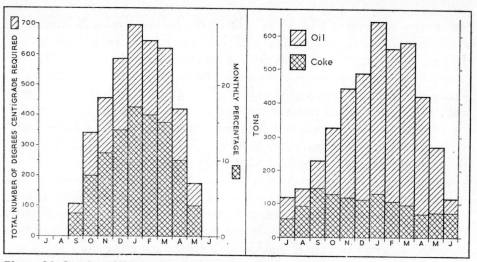

**Figure 24. Graphs of Winter Heating Requirements and Costs**

The left hand graph is based on the estimates of Håkan Lühr for lifting monthly temperatures to 17°C. The right hand diagram provides an actual illustration for a group of thirty blocks of flats in Norra Haga (Pohjois Haaga) Helsinki, and gives the average monthly consumption of oil and coke for the period 1958–64.

Some form of heating is required for about eleven months of the year in south Finland, though full-scale central heating is only necessary for nine months. Recent estimates by Håken Lühr, dealing with urban dwelling units and imported fuels, are based on a period of 7,920 hours annually. As an example, Lühr takes a six storey dwelling house, totalling 8,000 cu. m., and embracing thirty flats. The absolute volume of heat required depends on the heat efficiency of the fuel. Expressed in terms of coke, such a dwelling unit needs 75 tons annually; the steam coal equivalent is somewhat less; the oil fuel equivalent, 50·7 tons. The heating apparatus must be at least the minimum size needed to meet the peak demand for midwinter, so that the nature of the heating unit is a capital cost that must be balanced against the costs of fuel, labour and maintenance. Electricity, drawn from a central power supply, is another possible source of heat; but private generation from oil or solid fuel is much cheaper. In new housing estates, such as those in the satellite city of Tapiola, large-scale communal thermal heating plants are employed. Thermal heating also derives as a by-product of power plants, e.g., Sundholmen which supplies the central parts of Helsinki.

While the means of heating houses has been eased by new techniques, cost estimates have been reduced to almost mathematical simplicity. Heating engineers in Finland base their calculations on an indoor temperature of at least 17°C. In south Finland, where most of the population is concentrated, the mean annual temperature is 5°C. The task is accordingly to build up indoor temperature by the difference between the outdoor temperature and 17°C. Figure 24 (left) illustrates the number of degrees of warmth required monthly to compensate for temperature deficiencies in southern Finland. It is based on the mean monthly temperature conditions prevailing between 1931–60. Heat requirements are greatest between January and March, with the peak demand occurring towards the end of January.

Figure 24 (right) provides a precise illustration to set beside Håkan Lühr's example. It refers to a group of 32 residential blocks in a suburb of north Helsinki and the quantities of fuel required (reduced to coke equivalent) are averaged for eight years. A modest supply of heat is required throughout the summer for hot water. Although temperatures may be lower in February than in January, indoor daytime temperatures are lifted considerably by solar radiation.

Complementary to the production of heat is the prevention of heat loss. Heat transfers may take place through conduction, through radiation and by convection. In countries with winters such as Finland, heat loss results principally from the differences in temperature inside and outside of a building. Prevention of heat loss has been a concern of builders for a good many generations. It is a concern at the large-scale industrial level and small-scale domestic level.

At the industrial level, a country such as Finland is at a distinct disadvantage by comparison with countries in kinder climates. For example, its great paper and pulp factories must be built in closed structures; while in southern France, the digestors of the pulp plant may be merely covered by a roof. Kilometres of pipes for steam and water distribution require elaborate lagging or burying in the ground well below the level of frost penetration.

At the domestic level and in country districts, moss has been the traditional insulator in the construction of timber dwellings. An earth bank (*mullbänk*) behind the wainscoting and a double floor (*trossgolv*) are other old-established insulating devices. Today, a great range of insulating materials, including tarred paper, sawdust, felts, rock wool and glass wool, are employed as insulating blankets between walls, ceilings and floors. Double windows have been employed against winter cold for several generations. Formerly, they were fitted seasonally; but today, double-glazed units are automatically built in. The Finnish trend towards increasingly large glazed surfaces, which could be regarded as an expression of the urge to maximise light in a seasonally dark environment, has also affected heating demand. It has even encouraged the use of treble glazing. For example, buildings of the State Forestry Board north of Oulu have been equipped with triple-panel glass. Other experiments have been tried. Metal-coated window glass, which serves to reflect interior room heating, provides one example of a constructional development which is a new means of introducing heat economies. Such innovations introduced new elements to be included in formulae for assessing contemporary heating requirements.

## Winter Building

Building against winter has normally been a summer job. As building activities have become professionalized, Finland has found itself faced with another problem. Among the trades that suffer from the effects of winter, building and constructional work are outstanding. In them, winter unemployment and under-employment contrast with summer pressure of employment. The tendency remains, though it is being slowly adjusted. Both the high demand for buildings and the social urge to reduce seasonal unemployment have led to the lively

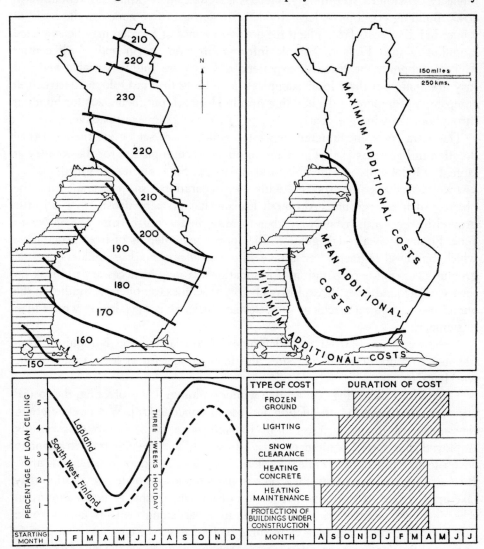

**Figure 25. Winter Building Conditions in Finland**

The four diagrams illustrate (i) Top left: depth in centimetres in normal winters for building foundations laid in frozen ground (after *Rakennustaito*, 1964, 15). (ii) Top right: regional differentiation of building costs (after *Rakennustaito*, 1964, 20). (iii) Bottom left: Building costs for constructing a brick and concrete block of apartments 5,000m³ in size in eight months. The heaviest costs are encountered three or four months after the starting month, so that the winter premium is especially pronounced if schemes are started in the autumn (Source: *Statens Institut för byggnadsforskning, Rapport* 86, Stockholm, 1962). (iv) Bottom right: Type and duration of extra winter building costs.

promotion of winter constructional programmes. It goes without saying that such activity is costly. It is an assault on winter, for which a toll must be paid [15].

Winter building costs in countries such as Finland reflect the duration and intensity of winter. Accordingly, there is a significant regional differentiation in costs. Building economists have divided Sweden into five zones on the basis of winter building costs [16]. The three northern zones of Sweden may be extended latitudinally into Finland. Sample information from north and south central Finland supports the Swedish experiences. Costs are highly variable and not easy to obtain; but three local examples – a building firm in Oulu, a construction company in Tampere, and a building firm in Helsinki, put their costs for building throughout the winter as nearly 50%, 30% and 15% higher respectively.

The extra costs encountered in winter building are set beside their seasonal duration in Figure 25 [17]. The diagram offers a rough picture for the country at large, but it conceals considerable local variations. Six costs are identified.

Two basic costs are associated with site preparation – snow clearance and the obstacle of frozen ground. Although Finland has no permafrost, frost is in the ground in the south from November to May; in the north from September to June. Figure 25 is a rough guide to the approximate depths of frost penetration which building engineers must take into consideration. For builders, frozen ground hampers the preparation of foundations. It may be necessary to break up the frozen ground layer by explosives before machines can operate. Studies in the winter use of digging machines suggest that efficiency is 15% less in winter than in summer.

A third cost arises from light deficiency. Artificial lighting is required from October to March on building sites and in buildings for at least a part of the working day.

Three forms of heating cost arise in winter building. There are, first, the special costs resulting from the production and use of concrete [18]. Winter concreting, the subject of intensive research in Finland since 1950, is now successfully employed. But special equipment must be used to heat the concrete, to maintain adequate air temperatures while it hardens, and, thus, to aid its freezing resistance. It takes normal concrete several weeks to harden and complete dehydration may take up to a year. Accordingly, reduction of hardening time is highly important where winter conditions are severe. The new hardening cements take a week: 'super-rapid' cement can achieve in three or four days the equivalent hardening of normal Portland cement in four weeks. Secondly, there are the general costs of heating buildings so that labourers can operate under conditions of adequate comfort. Thirdly, there are the capital and maintenance costs of the heating apparatus from simple coke baskets and naptha oil heaters to larger scale apparatus. An additional substantial element in winter building costs are the insulating structures and materials needed to enclose the area of operation. The practice of erecting insulating structures of plastic, paper and cardboard for cement hardening is increasingly common [19].

Entire buildings cocooned in order to facilitate winter building operations are impressive sights (see Plate 13). Winter building activities have increased steadily over the last decade; though, expressed in millions of cubic metres of buildings completed, winter still lags about a fifth behind the production during the summer months. Generally speaking, building site labour and building trade craftsmen cannot be transferred to factory jobs during the winter season. Otherwise, there might be room for experiment in transferring labour to the manufacture of assembly-line houses, since components for houses are manufactured without seasonal interruption. At least one firm (in Forssa, near Helsinki) claims that its annual output of 6,000 ready-made houses, designed for simple erection in the summer, is a more economic way of approaching the winter building situation.

## Fashions in Clothing

Winter calls for a special wardrobe. Different kinds and different quantities of clothes are needed. Particular attention has had to be paid to the susceptible extremities, so that footwear, gloves and ear muffs, have had to be devised. The Finnish winter wardrobe may be less picturesque than formerly, but it retains a marked seasonal distinction. Earlier travellers have left colourful descriptions of their sartorial adjustments to the Finnish winter. Generally speaking, they were more colourful and more exaggerated than those of the natives. William Coxe [20], entering from St. Petersburg, festooned himself in eighteenth century opulence; for Edward Clarke, crossing the Åland archipelago, there was no substitute for fur; Bayard Taylor sought a Lappish solution to the problem of keeping warm. All have left affectionately meticulous descriptions of their attire.

'To guard against the cold (wrote William Coxe), I clothed myself in a suit of Bath drugget, lined with flannel, two pairs of worsted stockings and slippers, over which boots were drawn well-lined with flannel and fur. These boots I generally wore in the carriage, but pulled off when I entered the house; and had the weather proved uncommonly severe, I was provided with a kind of sheep-skin pantaloons, the wool on the inside which reached to my hips and were large enough to enclose my boots; I wrapped round my body a great coat of blue nankeen, lined with lambskin and occasionally added a large pelisse or fur robe. I had a bear-skin muff, and my head was enveloped in a black-velvet cap, quilted with silk and cotton, which covered my cheeks, was tied under my chin, and might, if necessary, be drawn over the face.'

Edward Clarke [21] and his companions recorded that:

'Over our feet we had thick yarn stockings covered by stout leather boots, and over these again were boots made of the hides of reindeer, with the hair on the outside, and doubly lined with sheep-skin covered with black wool. We had, moreover, fur caps upon our heads, and bear-skin pelisses over our bodies, besides several flannel waistcoats; and upon our hands, gloves of sheep-skin, covered by double gloves of fur and wool.'

By comparison, Bayard Taylor was almost scientific in his approach.

'The *paesk* of reindeer skin,' he wrote, 'is the warmest covering for the body which could be devised. It is drawn over the head like a shirt, fitting closely around the neck and wrists, where it is generally trimmed with ermine, and reaching halfway below the knee. A thick woollen sash, wrapped first around the neck, the end then twisted together down to the waist, where they are passed tightly around the body and tied in front, not only increases the warmth and convenience of the garment, but gives it a highly picturesque appearance. Our sea otter caps, turned down so as to cover the ears and forehead, were fastened upon our heads with crimson handkerchieves, and our boas, of black and red squirrel tails, passed thrice around the neck, reached to the tips of our noses. Over our dogskin mittens, we drew gauntlets of reindeer skin' – add to this 'a pair of reindeer leggings and broad boat-shaped shoes, filled with dry soft hay and tightly bound round the ankles, and the ensemble is complete.'

Furs and skins have always played a generous role in the Finnish wardrobe. They continue to do so. In Ylitornio (Över Torneå), Brooke recorded the dress of the Finlanders as 'a loose open frock, of dark or grey cloth, reaching below the knees, and lined with sheepskin; a long narrow sash – frequently yellow – round the waist, keeping the garment, which was without buttons, close to the body. High, black, dogskin caps were very general; and to supply this warm appendage, some hundreds of the canine race . . . were slaughtered'. When Sir John Carr 'contemplated' Finland it was a country 'clad in fur'. For Selina Bunbury, it was 'the furry dress of the Finn peasant' that left its impression. Fur hats are a regulation military issue (for the Salvation Army, too, in black astrakhan). In midwinter, four out of five people in the streets of Helsinki will be wearing fur hats. Although Finland has a very substantial export of farm-bred mink, it has also a large import of furs for winter clothing.

There are changing and constant elements in the fashions of winter. Unfortunately, the traditional garments of the Lapp, which represent such an intimate and effective environmental adjustment, are being replaced by less satisfactory manufactured garments. The thigh boots of northern and eastern Finland, with their turned-up toes and laced-up tops, are still manufactured and still in demand; though they are less assiduously painted with tar preservative than they used to be. Leather knee-boots are a widespread feature. In winter, overshoes, overboots and galloshes are common. They belong to the era of rubber manufacture, as does the rubber boot that has often replaced the leather knee-boot. Hosiery has changed its form. Woollen stockings (formerly knitted at home from home-spun wool) have suffered decline rather than demise. The woollen goods industry, one of the oldest workshop industries in the country, has also experienced a general contraction since the widespread introduction of central heating. Because there are many influences at work affecting the purchase of woollen underwear, it would be difficult to ascribe the decline in sales entirely to new means of domestic heating. But it may be fairly claimed that this is one element in the contracting market. A comparison of the autumn season sales of woollen and woollen mixture pants by *Suomen Trikoo* [23], largest of the Finnish knitwear producers, illustrates the point. In 1956, sales of woollen pants totalled 49,650 pairs; in 1964, 24,090. The corresponding figures for woollen mixture pants were 10,070 and 3,270. Woollen manufacturers, seeking alternative markets, have achieved especial success with new type blankets and rugs.

New fabrics and new garments enter the scene. Skiing clothes, the basis for a new export trade, provide an example. Their manufacture is typical of the new scientific approach to winter clothing. An important objective in combating low temperature is to try and reduce the natural convection currents in the air – to immobilize as far as possible air molecules. It is possible to simulate the conditions achieved by the best insulated fur-bearing animals by producing materials in which 'dead air' is enclosed in a very restricted space. Loose fibrous material, such as cotton wool or kapok, layered between outer fabrics and packed to an optimum density of 4 lbs. per cubic foot, traps so-called 'dead air' and acts as a nearly perfect insulator. The principle of insulation has been known to the Lapp for a good many centuries, right down to the detail of the fine grasses with which he lines his skin shoes.

It need hardly be added that many changes in clothing are simply an attempt to give a West European or North American gloss to the wardrobe. Fashion may rule over winter and discomfiture may be a handmaiden willingly suffered.

## Food for Energy

A natural bodily reaction to cold is the increase of heat production by metabolism. In order to maintain the same body temperature, the lower temperatures of winter call for the closer control of heat and the greater control of heat production. Heat derived from the chemical energy released through the consumption of food and drink is of less importance if clothing and domestic heating are adequate. Forms of protection have become more efficient at the same time as supplies of food have become more reliable.

In former days, the time of the year when energy demands were greatest tended to be that when food supplies were least. The provision of adequate food to last the whole of the winter season was a major Finnish problem until the appearance of modern internal and external forms of communication. A country proverb records the end of March as the most critical time, 'When day and night are equal, hunger in the belly is greatest'. It was the same with fodder as with food. Eighteenth century husbandry books urged a more rational collection of fodder, from the outlands as well as from the meadows. The consequences of fodder shortage are recalled in the poorer quality of dairy products ('winter milk' and 'winter butter' are phrases from the past which are still used) as well as in the springtime condition of draught animals. A military report from Savo in the 1780's recorded 'the small, but strong horses' being 'exhausted in winter and rarely usable in spring'. Indeed, the age of domestic animals was commonly counted in the number of winters (not the number of years) that they had survived – thus *talviasvarsa* (a yearling) and *viidentoista talviais* (a horse fifteen winters old).

The revolution in fodder production has eliminated seasonal shortages. At the same time, a detailed study of food consumption by the rural population recently undertaken by Maja Pekkarinen, concludes that there are 'no great seasonal or regional variations in energy intake' [24]. Nevertheless, the conservation of food in summer for use in winter continues, with traditional methods remaining alongside new. The potato cellar, buried up to its eaves in the earth, is a feature of most country homes; though in some parts it takes the form of a small cellar reached by a trapdoor in the kitchen floor. Berries are bottled; mushrooms, preserved; cucumbers, pickled. Winter is marked by an absolute shortage of green vegetables; though deep freezing of domestic supplies is increasingly common. Meat and fish are still salted, smoked and dried against the winter needs. Winter itself provides natural outdoor refrigeration for keeping meat, fish and game. Even in cities, game birds and animals may be suspended from the balconies of flats until such time as they may be needed for consumption. John Atkinson commented on the markets 'of frozen provisions' and their relics may be still be found among the hardy stallholders even in the capital. Leopold von Buch, visiting Finnish Lapland in the early years of the nineteenth century, wrote of the Lapps as exposing reindeer milk to frost to 'preserve frozen pieces like cheese. When melted after a lapse of several months, this will still taste fresh and delicious' [25].

Most visitors to Finland have commented on the high consumption of spirits – commonly referred to as brandy, but currently sold as *akvavit* or illicitly distilled as *pontikka*. Strong drink was condoned in all of the classical travellers' accounts as an antidote to the inhuman winter. There is no correlation between climatic inclemency and sales of alcohol today, and no correlation between low winter temperatures and drunkenness. The sales statistics of the State Alcohol Monopoly show summer to be the season of peak demand; while offences for drunkenness are at a maximum at the same time. More people probably have more money to spend on liquor at this season of the year. In brief, alcohol does not seem to play any noticeably fortifying role in the struggle with winter. At the same time, purchases of tobacco, highest in the winter months, suggest its comforting virtues [26].

## A Matter of Acclimatisation

Until within living memory most Finns have lived very close to nature and have understood its changing phenomena with an almost sixth sense. Today, most are urban dwellers who face the problems of winter with the aid of science. In the space of a lifetime, a multitude of new facilities has become available to simplify and amplify the business of daily life in cold climates. These facilities are seen in improved forms of feeding, clothing and shelter. In fact, because the high standard of living makes it possible and the winter climate urges it many domestic amenities in Finland have been lifted to a higher level than those in most West European countries.

Winter is no respector of persons. The distance at which people can keep it at bay is not independent of the lengths of their purses. Yet, in Finland, the principles of the welfare state guarantee that the distance is adequate for the lowliest. And it is no longer the wealthy alone who seek winter escape from the sub-Arctic in sub-tropical retreats. The only problem is that the inhabitants of contemporary Finland are so accustomed to their artificial climates that many of them are no longer acclimatised to the natural condition of winter.

## BIBLIOGRAPHY

[1] cf. A. C. Burton and O. G. Edholm, *Man in a Cold Environment*, London, 1955.

[2] O. Kalela, On secular rhythms in the distributional dynamics of some European birds and mammals and its relation to winter conditions, *Ornis fennica*, 1950, 27.

[3] M. Eisentraut, *Der Winterschlaf*, Jena, 1956.

[4] R. Kristoffersson and P. Suomalainen, Studies on the Physiology of the hibernating Hedgehog, *Annales Academiae Scientarium Fennicae*, A, IV, 76, 80, 1964. We are grateful to Professor P. Suomalainen for his helpful comments on this section.

[5] P. Seiskari, On the winter ecology of the capercaillie (*Tetrao urogallus*) and the black grouse (*Lyrurus tetrix*) in Finland, *Papers on Game Research*, Helsinki, 1962, 22.

[6] J. Schefferus, *Lapponia*, Oxford, 1674.

[7] J. E. Smith (tr.) C. Linnaeus, *Journey to Lapland*, 2 Vols., London, 1811. See also, R. Helle, An investigation into reindeer husbandry in Finland, *Acta Löpponica Fenniae*, 5, Rovaniemi, 1966.

[8] E. Pulliainen, The appearance and behaviour of wolves in Finland during the period 1954–62, *Suomen riista*, 1962, 15; Studies on the wolf in Finland, *Annales zoologici Fennici*, 1965, 2.

[9] G. Pleijel and N. Lindquist, *Dagsljus – en orientering med litteraturförteckning*, Stockholm, 1947.

[10] N. Valonen, *Zur Geschichte der finnischen Wohnstuben*, Helsinki, 1963.

[11] *Puun käyttö*, 1922, 1938, 1953.

[12] M. Honkanen, Consumption of fuel, amount of work required and costs of heating farmhouses in Finland, 1960, *Suomen maataloustieteellisen seuran julkaisuja*, Helsinki, 1964.

[13] *Industridelegationens betänkande rörande industrialiseringens förutsättningar och åtgärder för dess främjande*, Helsingfors, 1961.

[14] H. Lühr, Bostadshusens värmekostnader, *Hufvuvudstadsbladet*, 1965.

[15] S. Houvila and S. E. Pihlajavaara, Principal features of the Finnish climate with special reference to winter building, *Valtion teknillinen tutkimuslaitos*, Helsinki, 1956, III, 2.

[16] F. Eriksson and J. A. Jonsson, Winterbyggnads-merkostnader i landets olika deler, *Statens Institut för byggnadsforskning, Rapport* 86, Stockholm, 1962, and F. Eriksson, Vinterbyggnad, *Statens nämnd för byggnadsforskning, Rapport*, Stockholm, 1957.

[17] F. Eriksson and S. Isotalo, *Rakennustaito*, Helsinki, 1964.

[18] A. Nykänen and S. Pihlajavaara, The hardening of concrete under winter concreting conditions, *Valtion teknillinen tutkimuslaitos*, Helsinki, 1958, 35.

[19] R. Pekkonen, *Rakennustaito*, Helsinki, 1965, 884–6.

[20] William Coxe, *Travels in Prussia, Russia, Sweden and Denmark*, London, 1803, III.

[21] E. Clarke, *op. cit.*

[22] Bayard Taylor, *op. cit.*

[23] A communication from Suomen Trikoo OY/AB, Tampere.

[24] Maja Pekkarinen, *Tutkimus maalaisväestön ravinnosta eräissä Itä- ja Länsi-Suomen pitäjissä*, Hämeenlinna, 1962.

[25] L. von Buch, *Travels in Norway and Lapland*, 1806–08, London, 1813.

[26] *Rural Consumption Investigation, 1959–60*, Helsinki, 1962. This was a survey of the accounts of 120 farmers and wage earners. Dr. Sakari Härö, of the Finnish Board of Health, has provided data for this section.

# The Exploitation of Winter

*The Time of the Runner*

In certain areas of activity, winter has offered opportunities which summer has denied. While it has hampered movement at sea, it has eased movement overland. In winter, frozen lake, bog and coastal bay open the possibility of more direct and speedier routes. At the same time, the rough details of the surface of the land are smoothed out, while local contours are invested with a new meaning. The opportunities offered by winter have been realized because of a simple device – the runner. The runner, expressed as sleigh and ski, has been employed for thousands of years. In days before mechanization, it generated less friction on ice and snow surfaces than the wheel. Given the runner, movement was quicker in winter than in summer. It speeded the chase. The runner also meant more comfortable movement. William Coxe spoke of the usual rate of sleigh travel two hundred years ago as six to eight miles an hour; but that was less important than the fact that 'the gliding of the carriages over the beaten snow was so easy as to be almost imperceptible'. He wrote of 'slumbering in my travelling coach as comfortably as in a bed'. So, too, did Arthur de Capell Brooke and his sleigh was accounted 'a better bed than we had been for some time accustomed to'.

Runners meant that loads could be transported more easily – logs from the forest, manure to the arable land, hay from the meadow sheds, boulders from the stream bed. The correspondence of *Strömrensningskommitten* from the early years of the nineteenth century makes regular reference to working on the ice in winter and shifting obstructive boulders over natural ice bridges [1]. In its modest way, winter assisted the maritime survey. C. N. af Schultén's autobiography has graphic descriptions of his survey team sounding the lead through ice holes in the skerries – with the unfortunate horses falling 'several times a day' through the weaker ice, 'which the worthy coastmen thought nothing of, but forced them up again immediately and work continued'! [2]. In addition, mapping the configuration of the skerries was undertaken in winter when the sea was frozen.

Sledge and ski have always been important for the harvesting and marketing of forest products. Indeed, the climax of the contemporary co-operation with winter is encountered in forestry; though it is rivalled by the employment of the runner for purely pleasurable purposes. The ski, bred of utility, has probably become the principal single symbol of recreation.

Most of the technical devices employed to use the opportunities offered by winter belong to a broader cultural area and are not indigenous to Finland. That they have been derived from Russian, Baltic and Scandinavian sources is probable from the nature and distribution of prehistoric relics. The same applies to the contemporary scene, with the variety of equipment used to capitalize on snow and ice having its origin in a number of different countries, among which Scandinavia and North America are principal.

> Syksyn selkää pestään,
> talvi sillat laittaa,
> nyt se keli kestää,
> nythän päästään metsiin,
> halonhakku alkaa, luistaa tukkityö.

The poetic and the practical appreciation of winter are wedded in Larin Kyösti's poem on the coming of the first snow – *Ensi lumen tullessa.* 'Autumn's back is washed clean by it, the bridges of winter are built, now the ice bears anew, the way to the woods is open, the woodsman's axe resounds and the timber sledge glides again.'

## The Art of Hunting

The first winter bonus to be appreciated was probably hunting. Snow and ice gave men a new mobility in relation to animals which could now more easily be traced by their spoors in the snow. At this time of the year their value as food was also enhanced and their skins were at their best. In earliest times, the pelteries were the main income of the country. However, the retreat of the natural frontier before advancing settlement meant that already by the eighteenth century, fur production had declined to insignificance. When Arthur de Capell Brooke passed through the Tornio valley, he noted that furs were neither so good nor so cheap as in London. But around the margins of the settled zone, they continued to make an incidental contribution.

Hunting and trapping continue to provide a little income for the Lapps and their former skill was recorded by a good many travellers just before the final decline set in. The wild reindeer was the chief quarry. It was driven into elaborate pitfalls and traps during the autumn migrations, but hunted on skis in the open fell in winter. Helmer Tegengren, in an historical appreciation of the Finnish Lapps, refers to 24 February as the day when the formal chase of wild reindeer began [3]. It continued until the end of April. Originally, the beaver was the principal animal trapped in winter. It was caught in a variety of nets and cages which were placed under the ice near to the beavers' huts. The Lapps also had their especial winter traps for the fox and wolverine. The wolf was hunted in order to protect domestic stock. The climax of the winter hunting was the bear hunt. For the Lapps, it was a rite accompanied by magic ceremonies as well as a sport. Down to 1900, bear hunting was an intermittent pursuit over the greater part of Finland. Finnish military records recall a bear hunt in Karelia by the Kuopio battalion in 1890–1. Participants travelled 860 km. on skis in 29 days and shot seven bears.

Around the coast, the seal has played a role in late winter hunting since men first followed the edge of the retreating Pleistocene ice sheet [4]. The seal was basic to the original occupation of the Åland archipelago. *Phoca groenlandica*, flourishing in the cooler waters of the late-glacial Yoldia Sea, provided skins for clothing, food for eating and oil for light and fuel.

Seal hunting enters into some of the earliest records of Ostrobothnia, where a tithe of the catch was allotted to the church. In the Vaasa *skärgård*, the hunting season opened traditionally on Lady Day and ended in mid-May. Hunting continued until mid-June in the skerries off Kemi and Tornio. It mobilized the interest of most of the able-bodied men of the island communities during the spring-winter. Sometimes, as in the parish of Malax in the early eighteenth century, it was one of the main sources of income. As soon as country vicars began to make general observations in their church books, a scatter of references to sealing appeared. In Malax, for example, 1750 was described as a poor seal year; in 1752, seals were considered abundant in the outer skerries; 1757 was marked by 'fierce cold, so that the seals left the northern gulf for southern waters'. Indeed, there emerged a general pattern of hunting in southern waters (*Södersjön*, as they were called) during colder winters and northern waters (*Norrbottnen*) during milder winters [5].

A boat's crew usually consisted of 6–8 men and the average expedition lasted 10–12 weeks. To fit out and provision such an undertaking was a considerable enterprise in its own right. Edward Clarke had encountered seal hunters – 'expert marksmen . . . creeping about among the rocks with their rifle-barrelled guns, watching for the appearance of a seal's head through an aperture in the ice'. A catch of ten seals per man was regarded as good. A single seal might weigh 50–60 kg. and yield 30–35 kg. of fat.

Among individual parishes, Bergö was the largest centre of sealing during the early nineteenth century [6]. According to the comparative statistics assembled by C. C. Böcker in the 1830's, 60% of the income of Bergö derived from sealing;

while an estimate from 1851 still placed it at more than 50%. In that year, the newspaper *Ilmarinen* reported Bergö's springtime harvest to be 500 seals. Seal fat and seal oil were barrelled for export mostly to Sweden; skins had a wider market. As many as 100 hunters, including many from the mainland, might go out to Bergö Gaddar in the 1880's and every bunk in the fishermen's cabins of the outer skerries might be occupied. Prices for the products might rise steadily, but the climax of the enterprise had already been realised and the beginnings of decline were apparent. There were several reasons. First, there were the hazards and discomfitures of an enterprise in a virtual Arctic microcosm. Secondly, the number of seals showed a decline. Thirdly, an easier living could be obtained from other activities, especially from agriculture, which could no longer be left seasonally to the womenfolk.

Seal hunting only survives in some of the Ostrobothnian parishes. In the spring winter of 1962, four boats put out from Vaasa *skärgård* and they were followed at a later stage by several motor boats journeying northwards in May. Yet hunters report hundreds of seals clustered closely together on the ice edge [7]. Estimates suggest a possible Baltic population of 20,000. The reverse of the coin is that they probably consume 134 tons of fish a day – and perhaps as much as 50,000 tons a year (which is as big as the total annual Finnish fish catch in the Baltic). But all that the contemporary visitor sees of an industry which has moved men since remote antiquity is the occasional 'shadow' of a sealskin upon a boat-house door – its outline stained into the wood by the fat when it was stretched for drying.

As soon as sealing ceased to be economically significant to the skerry people, it declined. Unlike the hunting of other creatures it did not become a sport. For the contemporary sportsman, it is the lesser creatures that remain the principal winter quarry. The situation is summed up in Alexis Kivi's novel *Seven Brothers* [8]. 'Gun in hand (they) ski'd around the forest, and their bullets felled white-furred hares under the snow-clad trees, felled a male capercaillie as, with ruffled feathers and heavy with the cold, it sat on the branch of a bearded spruce.' A very exceptional form of hunting appears to have been practised on the bays around Helsinki in the early years of the century, where Rosalind Travers participated in a drag hunt over the March snows on the bays [9].

Winter fishing probably means more than hunting. It is an art which is still practised commercially, but which is much more widely pursued as a pastime. A little commercial seine fishing through ice holes is found in both the archipelagoes, where Baltic herring are netted, and in the lakes where the *muikku* (*Coregonus albula*) is sought. It retains a traditional character, with parallels from the days of Olaus Magnus. In his *History* he wrote of Bothnian fishermen opening up 'great holes, some eight or ten foot broad, and 150 to 200 paces from each other', between which cords and nets were drawn to yield 'whole wagon loads' of fish. Today, teams operating along the coast may consist of up to a dozen men, but it is unusual to find more than three or four operating together in the lakes. The ice holes are sawn above known fishing grounds. The seine is usually drawn over the winch by horses; but tractors are also employed.

As a means of recreation, ice hole fishing has assumed almost 'Middle West' proportions. Surrounded by the paraphernalia of tents, windproof clothing, heating equipment and even parked cars, winter fishermen extract a curious pleasure out of what was formerly an uncomfortable necessity. Plate 9 shows a typical *pilkkijä*, or ice hole fisherman.

## The Role of the Sledge

The emergence of the sledge in Finland is inseparable from its development in Scandinavia and Russia [10]. The oldest sledges would seem to have used a single runner. The prototype is the 'keel' or runner of the boat sledge found in a peat bog at Laukaa in Häme, and which has a close affinity to Swedish relics found at Ragunda in Jämtland and Delsbo in Hälsingland. The single-runnered sledge was probably used for hunting and a form of it was encountered until recent years in north and east Finland. U. T. Sirelius has reconstructed a sketch of a single-runnered, boat-shaped sledge from Korpiselkä in Karelia. The origins of the single-runner probably belong to the late Stone or early Bronze Age. Related relics have been recovered from over thirty different sites, scattered as widely as Inari in the north and Turku archipelago in the south. Pollen analysis gives to the oldest of them, a runner from Heinola, an age of 7,500 years. Such remains pre-date those of any known skis.

The hunting sledge had a distinctive name which was already committed to paper as early as 1520 – *ackebotten*. While men originally pulled these sledges, dogs may also have been harnessed to them. Jakob Fellman, during his north Finnish journeys of the later nineteenth century, made reference to dog sleighs (*ahkio*) in east Karelia. The *ahkio*, or man-drawn sled, remains an essential piece of military equipment.

The Lapp sledge, traditionally pulled by the reindeer, is one of a single-runner type; though there are variations upon it. The reindeer was probably domesticated in northern Europe for draught purposes by the Lapps. Only the Lapps employ single-draught reindeer, though pairs are used among the Samoyed. Arthur Dillon [11] described the usual type of Lapp sledge or *pulkka* as resembling

'a small sea-boat the stern of which has been cut off and replaced by an upright board. It is klinker built, with a broad keel, and sufficiently high behind to support the back. From stem to stern it is scarcely more than four feet long, and just wide enough to admit one person of moderate dimensions. It is dragged by a trace of deerskin'.

Paul du Chaillu [12] found that Lapp sleighs

'looked exactly like little tiny boats . . . made of narrow fir-tree planks . . . about seven feet long and 2½ feet in width at the end . . . They had keels like sailing boats; these were very strong and about four inches wide . . . The higher the keel is the quicker the sleigh can go'.

Brooke did not enjoy travelling in them and complained of 'being cooped up in a machine as narrow as a coffin'. In former times, special *pulkat* were made with fitted lids for transporting food.

The single runner is also a feature found in other primitive vehicles. The so-called guide-runner, consisting of a slightly hollowed platform behind an up-turned ski-like front, has been regularly used to transport casks and other containers. A piece of equipment of a rather similar character is employed to transport seal-hunters' boats in the inner reaches of the Gulf of Finland. The Bothnian seal-shooter's runner, on which a gun is mounted and a white sail hoisted to conceal the hunter, uses a similar principle.

Although less old than single-runner vehicles, built-up sledges have a long history [13]. Runners discovered in peatlands as widely scattered as Kuortane, Pihtipudas, Rautalampi and Kiuruvesi, are parts of some proto built-up sledge. The runners are pitted with uniformly patterned holes, probably used to fix the struts on which the body of the sledge was supported. The arrangement of the strut holes has a different pattern in runners found in Alavus, Jalasjärvi and Saarijärvi (in southern Ostrobothnia). Both illustrate the variety of sleigh models that was emerging at an early stage in the occupation of Finland. In date, these early finds of runners are attributed to the Comb Ceramic phase of prehistoric development (*c.* 3000–2000 B.C.). The built-up sledges were of a heavier and more substantial character than the single-runner vehicles. Both reindeer and dogs may have been employed in drawing them.

Ski-sledges, also built up above the ground level, have long and upturned runners. The runners were usually bent into this shape by pressure. Arthur Dillon, describing a north Bothnian farmhouse in 1840, wrote that '. . . the runners of a sledge were receiving the peculiar curve that distinguishes them in Finland' [14]. Carl Linnaeus sketched a sledge of this character in the vicinity of Oulu. It was a box structure, built on runners, 'with a cross board to rest the feet against' [15]. Finnish specialists usually refer to this type of sledge as 'East Finnish' in form.

The ski-sledge is a heavier vehicle, and was probably horse-drawn from the beginning. Its origin would seem to be later than other sledge forms and the use of the horse to draw it may suggest Russian provenance. All of the Kalevalan heroes used horse-drawn sleighs. Ilmarinen, the smith, made his journey home from Pohjola in such a sleigh [16] –

> Loudly rang the iron runners,
> And the frame of birch resounded,
> And the curving laths were rattling,
> Shaking was the cherry collar,
> And the whiplash whistled loudly,
> And the rings of copper shaking,
> As the noble horse sprang forward.

The caravanseraies of horse-drawn sleighs which moved overland and oversea have been described by William Coxe and Edward Clarke respectively. William Coxe was journeying westwards from Viipuri [17]. He wrote that:

'Our train consisted of eight sledges, including those appropriated to the baggage; as on account of the narrowness of the roads each person had a separate carriage. Various kinds of sledges are used in this country; some are entirely closed, others quite open, those which we employed were partly open and partly covered. A sledge of this sort is shaped like a cradle; the tilt which projects two feet, was open in the front, but provided with curtains which might be drawn and tied together whenever the weather was severe. The outside was secured with matting and oil-skin, and the inside with coarse cloth . . . Each sledge was drawn by two horses . . . harnessed one before the other.'

The winter retinue encountered by Edward Clarke, passing from Åland to Kumlinge, was accompanying the Swedish post [18].

'First went a party of scouts, as pioneers, proving the ice with their safety pikes. Then came the Swedish post to Finland, the mail bags, fastened upon a very small sledge, being drawn by a single man.  Then followed another party of scouts, with their pikes as before; and, after these men, my own sledge . . . Next advanced a promiscuous multitude of travellers without much order or caution, preceding their respective sledges, and attentive only to the preserving of a proper distance from each other, so as not to huddle together on any one spot; and, behind all these, another party of the peasants ready for any work in which their assistance might be required . . . the whole retinue reached to a distance of two English miles.'

The party covered as much as 35 miles in a day, a circuituous route having to be followed for reasons of security. Apart from intermittent alarms, Clarke was much entertained by 'the appearance of such a numerous host marching over the abyss of water'.

A single man also drew the post sleigh on less frequented routes such as that between Kotka and the Island of Suursaari (Högland) in the Finnish Gulf. The Post Museum in Helsinki houses this smallish sleigh, with leather bags three feet square in a capacious net which would make them more easy to retrieve in event of accident. The sleigh was especially designed for use in *kelirikko*, when the going was bad.

Sledge forms proliferated in the period immediately preceding mechanically propelled vehicles. A variety of sledges for timber transport emerged. In Ostrobothnia, a short sledge was found, to which the heavier ends of the logs were lashed, leaving the lighter ends to trail the ground. Guide runners were also used in Ostrobothnia to ease the transport of timber. Double sledges, commonly linked together by chains or a beam continue to be employed for timber transport. Articulated sledges, heavily tarred and drawn by tractors, are common features of the lumbering scene. The grooved tracks in which they move are watered in order to produce a smooth icy surface.

The sledge as a vehicle for personal transport acquired an elaborate variety of superstructures. In their initial stages, sledges were probably constructed for one person; but two-passenger sledges are recorded in *Kalevala*. Three or four-passenger sledges were emerging in the seventeenth century. Arthur de Capell Brooke enjoyed [19]

'... the Finlander's sledge ... very long, broad, and capacious, with a high back-board. In front there is a seat for the driver; and the space between this and the extremity of the sledge contains the luggage.'

To open sledges were added closed sledges. Four-seater coaches or *kupeer* [20] appear to have been lifted off their wheel axles and planted on runners. Elaborate carpentering, carving, painting and upholstering adorned the personal sleighs, and the harness of the horse assumed no less elaboration. The horse bow – painted, carved and varnished; the bearskin collar tucked beneath it; the variety of sleigh-bells made it an equipage which brought colour to the winter countryside [21]. A few of these relics from the recent past have been gathered in museums; but many decay in barns.

Sledge carts are still widely employed. They were invaluable for commodity transport in earlier times. Approaching Tornio, Linnaeus observed 'a carriage called a *stötting* ... for bringing home wood for fuel in winter over the ice and snow'. It was made of birchwood, was 3½ feet long and resembled a sledge. The high *vinterskrinda*, or hay sleigh, is another example. Today, sledge carts are most commonly used for farm work.

A snow vehicle of recent historical origin, which is still widely used, but the employment of which has declined rapidly since the coming of motor transport is the chair-sled (Sw. *sparkstötting*; F. *potkukelkka*). The chair-sled, propelled on its runners much the same as a scooter, is a swift and practical means of transport in the countryside. The runners were originally of wood, but for the last two generations have been made of steel. Those who use this type of vehicle have normally worn an iron plate strapped to the sole of the left shoe. Formerly, all smiths made these 'iron shoes' (F. *rautikas*; Sw. *isbrodd*) or 'ice shoes' (F. *jääkengät*) as they were also known. The *sparkstötting* is a practical method of transport which distributes the weight of the user over a relatively large surface area, making it especially suitable for employment in the archipelagoes. Its origin is much debated; but it would seem to belong to the middle of the nineteenth century and to the Swedish province of Norrland [22]. The *sparkstötting* found its way to the Hämeenlinna battalion in the 1880's. It has a number of possible ancestors. The *stolpkälke*, a platform on runners with two handles, designed for the transport of commodities, is probably one of them. Developments of the *sparkstötting* took place along the Bothnian coast. A cross bar linked the handles, the broader wooden runners were mounted on iron (then replaced by steel), the 'seat' below the handles was shifted forward (so that the long flexible runners could be used more effectively for steering). The *sparkstötting* is found on most Finnish farms and in the possession of most families living in country areas, but it has disappeared from the streets of bigger cities in the last generation. It may serve the purpose of a perambulator (perambulators are also mounted on runners in winter), of a bicycle and of a wheelbarrow. It has been estimated that, with a light load, it is possible to cover 100 km. a day on the *sparkstötting*. In spite of the rise of other means of transport, they continue to be manufactured, principally as sporting equipment for children, in at least one sizeable factory – Joutjärvi Oy, in Lahti, the output of which has averaged over 16,000 annually for the last eight years [23].

The ultimate logic of a motorized age is to apply the ski to vehicles driven by internal combustion. The application of skis to light aircraft gives to them an even wider manoeuvrability than the summer use of floats. The snowmobile, employing front skis and rear caterpillar traction, is employed locally in north Finland though not as widely as in adjacent Norway and Sweden. Tractor sleighs are widely used in lumbering operations; though they cannot be employed on slopes exceeding three or four degrees. In lumbering areas, all sorts of buildings and equipment are mounted on runners – from caravans to power-driven saws. At the personal level, the ultimate development is the snow scooter, capable of moving cross country at 10 m.p.h. and of carrying a load several times as big as the 150 lbs. carried by the draught reindeer.

## The Place of the Ski

Finns have been virtually born on skis. Historically, skis are some of the oldest pieces of equipment found in the country. Contemporarily, they are a part of the nursery. In the countryside, most children's school journeys are made on skis. It is not possible to creep to school snail-wise in a Finnish winter.

The ski has been employed in Finland for thousands of years. As in the other countries of Norden, some of the oldest artifacts have been recovered from boglands [24]. The peat bogs of Finland have yielded a scatter of prehistoric skis from a number of districts. Pollen analysis gives a date of 4,000 years to the peat in which skis have been recovered from Kinnula, in north Häme; 3,500 years, to remains from Riihimäki. Prehistoric skis and ski-like remains have been recovered from more than sixty widely distributed sites. They include skis with raised footrests (140 cm. deep in peatland in Viitassaari, north Häme), flat-bottomed skis with decorated motifs from the early Middle Ages (from Kemijärvi), skis with runners almost as broad as the underside of the ski (from Liminka, and perhaps 2,000 years old), skis with runners of narrower width (from Muola in the Karelian isthmus). The finest and longest skis (131 cm.) have been found near Gamla Karleby. 'Giants' shoes', as they are called, have also been recovered in Lapinlahti (in Savo). They are a broader, hollowed out wooden type of ski which may have been used for other purposes.

The Finnish word for ski is *suksi* and it is generally regarded as of Uralic origin [25]. It is a word which has been transmitted to Finland from the east Finnish language. The Scandinavian word *ski* is probably a modification of it. There is a completely different Finnish word for the action of skiing – *hiihtää* (N. *gå på ski;* Sw. *löpa på skidor*): to ski. For the English, the word was probably first defined in Gustaf Widegren's *Svenskt och Engelskt Lexicon* (Stockholm, 1788) – '*Skid*, a kind of scate or wooden shoe on which they slide over the snow; *Lopa på skid*, to slide on scates.'

The ski entered the earliest Finnish folk-lore. In *Kalevala*, Lemminkäinen engaged in a strenuous hunt on skis for Hiisi's elk. In the medieval ballad of Bishop Henry's death, Lalli, the assassin, travelled on skis. In the thirteenth rune of *Kalevala*, a distinction is made between two different types of skis – a shorter and a longer.

> Ei lyly lykittävänä,
> Kalhu kannan löytävänä

The longer ski (*suksi* or *lyly*) was worn upon the left foot: the shorter (*kalhu*), upon the right. The shorter ski, also known by half a dozen other dialect words, was used for propulsion and commonly had a skin or partial skin covering. Lemminkäinen's skiing equipment was made by northern craftsmen.

> Lyylikki, a shaper of left skis,
>   Kauppi, maker of right skis
> Fashioned the left ski during the autumn,
>   shaped the right ski during the winter:
> One day carved a ski pole, the next he carved a disk.
> He made the left ski for pushing,
>   the right ski for stamping the heel on.
> He got the shafts of the ski poles ready,
>   the disks fitted.
> The shaft of the pole cost an otter skin,
>   the disk a reddish fox skin.
> He greased the skis with fat,
>   greased them thickly with reindeer fat [26].

In Ostrobothnia, the method of using the *lyly* and *kalhu* bore the name *spark-skidning* (in Finnish, *potkuhiihto*), perhaps ski-scooting. Such skis had largely died out by the end of the nineteenth century, save in the remoter north and in east Karelia; though Mrs. Alec Tweedie, instructing the English on the nature of skis in 1894 commented [27] – 'in Finland one ski is much longer than the other, and that one is usually quite flat.'

Only in limited areas in north Finland were two ski sticks traditionally employed. The Karelians, from whose homeland most Finnish skiing practices have stemmed, used only one (*suksensauva*). The Lapps also used one stick only, probably the herdsman's staff in its original role. For the English, the people of northern Scandinavia (*Nordkalotten*, as it is called today) were commonly called *Skrid Finnar* (from *skride*, to glide or slide). They were depicted in a number of early texts. Olaus Magnus, writing of *Scricfinnia* ('which hath one corner that stretcheth southward and toward the Bothnick Sea') described the inhabitants in the mid-sixteenth century as having 'their feet fastened to crooked pieces of wood, made plain and bended like a bow in the fore part; and by these they can at their pleasure transport themselves upward, downward, or obliquely, over the tops of snow'. Skiers were illustrated in the German edition of his *History*. Johannes Schefferus' *Lapponia* had illustrations of the diversions of the Lapps upon skis; while Arthur de Capell Brooke must have brought some of the first 'snow skates' to enter Britain from those parts.

Most skis have been made of birchwood. Spruce has also been used, but only particular trees have been regarded as suitable. Pine trees used for ski-making have borne the name *lylymänty* (in Swedish, *tjurtall*). The most sought after have been trees the trunks of which have split open to reveal the hard inner core beneath the softer outer layers.

Well defined regional distinctions in ski forms and ski names existed before the rise of factory production. The Lapps, for example, had their own type of relatively long skis, pointed at both ends and with a raised footpiece, which they made from birch or spruce. In Torne valley, skis were broader at the point and shorter than skis employed in Oulu valley – a difference explained deterministically by Hugo Sandberg in response to the wooded rocky country of the former and flat peaty wastes of the latter. Broader skis evolved in the archipelago for spreading the weight over the yielding surface of the ice (*saaristokalastajain suksi*); likewise, for use in crossing lakes (*järvisuksi*). O. A. Burman, in a regulation about skis to the Royal Helsinge Regiment of 1806, directed attention to the need for different skis for different terrains and contrasted the *skär-skidor* of Paldtamo ($3\frac{1}{2}$ *tum* or inches, broad) with the *snö-skidor* of West Uusimaa ($7\frac{1}{2}$ *tum* broad). Paul du Chaillu, visiting Finnish Lapland in the late 1890's, encountered several types of 'skees or the queer snowshoes of the north'. There were 'short ones used in the forest . . . where trees are close together'; long ones, for use on soft snow 'so that they can bear up the weight of a man and not sink too deeply'; skis faced with sealskin, 'used in spring when the snow is soft and becomes watery; the skin prevents the snow from sticking to the ski'.

The winter fishermen of the Ostrobothnian coast diverted Joseph Acerbi with their skiing ability [28]. He wrote of them that

'. . . they scour the ice on long wooden pattens, and shove themselves along with a pole they hold in their hands. The velocity of their progress is almost incredible; and the wonderful celerity of motion in their bodies, without the smallest perceptible action in their legs (for they use only their arms) forms a very striking sight.'

Acerbi tried to ski himself – without great success.

## *The Birth of Winter Sports*

The 1880's were a critical period in the re-appraisal of the ski. By the last quarter of the nineteenth century, the frontier of employment of the ski for working purposes had shifted largely to the interior. Referring to the parish of Hauho in Häme, T. Itkonen has commented that in the 1880's it was rare to see a ski save outside the huts of foresters, who used them for the journey to and from work. Itkonen gave as the boundary of the area between the use and non-use of skis, the line linking Vaasa-Jyväskylä-Heinola-Lappeenranta-Käkisalmi. A contributor to *Finsk Militär Tidskrift* in 1898 commented that plenty of people could remember the time when most churchgoers went on skis and there might be several hundred pairs stuck into the snow along the path that led to the church. The ski reached its nadir as an item of military equipment at the same time as it disappeared for other purposes. There was, indeed, some debate in military journals as to the comparative value of snowshoes and 160 pairs of snowshoes were imported from Canada for the army. The restoration of the ski as an item of military equipment was urged. With its aid, it was impressed, journeys of 80–100 miles a day could be achieved [29].

Revival of interest in the ski was started by two events which commanded widespread attention in Scandinavia. First, were the exploits of the Finnish-born A. E. Nordenskiöld. Nordenskiöld, who had emigrated to Sweden, demonstrated the effectiveness of skis on a remarkable Greenland journey where, together with two Lapps, he covered 460 kms. in 57 hours. The indispensability of the ski and the sleigh for polar exploration were further demonstrated in his scientific journey through the North-East Passage [30]. Secondly, and even more influential, was Fritjof Nansen's crossing of Greenland by ski and sleigh in 1888 [31]. It provided the model for all subsequent polar explorers. To simulate the epics (or, at least the training) of these two men became an immediate and popular recreation. In countries where winter forbade the new open-air ball games that were gaining popularity in western Europe, skiing provided a logical alternative.

Long-distance skiing began as a sport in Norway, Sweden and Finland almost simultaneously [32]. The first major competition, named after A. E. Nordenskiöld, was held in Sweden on 3–4 April 1884, and took place over a 220 km. course in Nordmark. But already in 1879, there had been Finnish skiing competitions in Tyrnävä; in Oulu in 1881; in Orimattila in 1883–4. The most unexpected places set skiing competitions in motion – Jaakkima in 1885; Sortavala and Impilahti, in 1886; Helsinki, the same year. In 1889, O. M. Reuter, in a guidebook published for the Tourist Society of Finland, referred to skiing as a leading sport:

'les courses sur raquettes, planches étroites longues de six pieds environ; au moyen desquelles on glisse légèrement à la surface des neiges profondes à raison de 10 à 14 kilometres à l'heure en effectuant des glissades vertigineuses le long des pentes; glissades au cours desquelles un bond de 10 mètres par dessus quelque fossé n'a rien qui étonne un coureur exercé.'

12. Horse transport of logs, using the jointed sleigh.

13. A building under construction with its protective covering against low temperature.

14. South Harbour, Helsinki during March.

15. The army stands at ease.

16. A children's ice hill.

But it is to the competition held in Oulu in 1891 that attention is directed as the starting point of Finland's new era. A photograph in the Finnish War Museum of the Oulu Battalion on skis in 1895 illustrates the restoration in the same area of military interest in this equipment. Modern skiing in Finland was weaned in the decade which followed, when a score of places besides Oulu initiated competitions. Finland began to send skiing teams to international meetings; permanent local societies were established; ski exhibitions were held and, in 1907, the Finnish Skiing Society (*Suomen Hiihtoliitto*) was born. From the beginning of the renaissance, women participated in the sport. Two hundred years earlier, J. F. Regnard had commented – 'les femmes ne sont pas moins adroites que les hommes à se servir de ces planches' [33].

The widening circle of participation, the diversification of competitive events and the multiplication of competitions have led to a contemporary situation in which a winter recreation of national magnitude has come into being. To cross-country skiing competitions has been added ski-jumping. Today, there are over 1,000 ski jumps scattered throughout the country. Nearly a hundred of them exceed a hundred feet in height. They include some of the loftiest in the world.

Norway's Holmenkollen competition was first emulated in Finland at Puijo Hill in Kuopio; but in 1926, the national competition was transferred to the Salpausselkä site at Lahti. The Salpausselkä gathering, usually held during the first week of March, is the climax of a year which now lists a programme of 250 official meetings. The programme opens during the first week of December in Kuusamo and finishes in Muonio in mid-April. Puijo retains a late February place in it and the competitors retreat northwards as the spring-winter sun gathers warmth. Coastal Kokkola yields finally to Lapland's Ounasvaara and Rukatunturi before the snow melts. Participants in the competitions are numbered by their hundred; spectators, by their thousands. It is claimed that the population of Lahti (1966, 85,000) is doubled during the games.

Behind the competitors in the national picture there are tens of thousands from whom they have been selected. Skiing instruction is carefully graduated for all ages and stages, and much of the enterprise focuses upon *Suomen Latu. Latu* is the Finnish word for the track or spoor (Swedish *skidspår*) left by the ski in the snow. The word is also found, with variants, in the Lappish language. Today, it has acquired an additional meaning – the marked cross-country track followed by skiers on their weekend outings. A million Finns have earned proficiency certificates from *Suomen Latu*. Special ski excursion days are celebrated (*laturetket*), when mass long distance treks are held. Each year, more than a hundred treks are held and as many as 4,000 skiers may participate in any one of them. More than 100,000 participants may share the exercises annually. Propaganda skiing treks and marathon journeys are also organized.

Almost everywhere in Finland, save in the central parts of the capital, it is possible to begin skiing at the front door. Theoretically, there is nothing to interrupt a midwinter journey on skis from the south coast to the Norwegian border. Finnish skiing is mostly cross-country, because the greater part of the country lacks considerable elevations. The coastal zone also has its skiing attractions, for example, the ice grottoes and caverns of the skerries. Edward Clarke's boatmen found one as a berth for their vessel . . . 'hung with pendant icycles and spangling crystal gems – the palace of the seals and temple of their amours'!

For most young and able people skiing holidays have become an integral part of life. Since the winter of 1933–4, the round of the year in educational institutions has been characterized by a late winter skiing break of seven working days. These holidays, arranged at the discretion of the school rectors between 21 February and 5 March, are taken later in north Finland than in the south. The most popular period for the skiing holiday is from late February to early April, when the sun is gaining altitude; though even *Kaamosaika* (the mid-winter twilight time) is advertized as a tourist attraction! The most popular holiday areas are the high fells or tunturit of Lapland. The Lapland fells are favoured for a second reason. They lie on the margins of the tree line, so that the timber which obstructs skiers over most of Finland is missing. Civil servants as well as employees of large companies are encouraged to take winter holidays (*talvilomat*), receiving 50% additional leave if they take their vacations out of the summer season.

Skiing centres with hotel and tourist hut facilities are developing rapidly. The economics of their existence are more sound if they can operate both a summer and a winter season. Farmhouse accommodation is also employed, expecially on the extended ski tours (*eräretki*) that are arranged for limited groups through the northern wildernesses. Even the President of Finland makes an annual 200 km. *retki* in Lapland. Three week excursions, covering 600 km. around the perimeter of Lake Inari, illustrate the most elaborate of the exercises. The rise of skiing centres implies the provision of a range of other amenities. Ski lifts are being multiplied, although they can have only a limited function in Finland. Lapps and reindeer are mustered to supply local colour at such centres as Pallastunturi. Even in the south, winter playgrounds such as Pitkävuori (near Jyväskylä), Aulanko (near Hämeenlinna) and Kaipola in Jämsä (with its ski lift, slalom slope and 'snow guns' to guarantee snow) illustrate the fact that there is money in winter.

Not least in interest, skiing has generated a ski-manufacturing industry. The distribution of factories was already illustrated in the third *Atlas of Finland* (1925), when factories in Oulu, Jyväskylä, Vimpele and Porvoo were identified. Today there are over a score of factories turning out 2,500 pairs or more a year, independently of workshops with a smaller output. The largest factories are those of *Esko Järvinen* in Lahti (output 120,000 pairs p.a.) and *Urheiluaitta* at Porvoo (output 60,000 pairs p.a.) [34]. Finland's total annual production is 450,000–500,000 pairs. It embraces an immense range of laminated and steel-edged skis which have a market abroad as well as at home. Export averages 50,000 pairs a year, but the potential market for Finnish skis in the U.S.S.R. has scarcely been touched. Not surprisingly, skis have an honourable place in the Sports Museum at the Olympic Stadium – from prehistoric relics, through specially decorated bridal skis to the skis of now legendary Finnish champions and of presidential enthusiasts. Ski boots have become a leading line for such shoe manufacturers as *Åström* in Oulu, *Aaltonen* in Tampere and *Mono* in Lahti; while companies such as *Reima-Pukine* in Kankaanpää produce 40,000 pairs of ski pants a year independently of anoraks and other winter sports clothing. Today, there is even more cause for raising a hymn to skiing than when Oscar Merikanto composed his *Hiihtäjän hymni* for *Suomen Urheilulehti* in 1905.

Finland is not one of the mid-twentieth century winter playgrounds of Europe. Yet, in its own right, it can claim to be a winter sporting land of international stature. The ski is native to Finland, conceived by craft out of necessity. The equipment associated with skiing, developed by both art and artifice, commands a growing attention in a European, let alone a North American market. 'At the turn of the year, a good pair of skis is worth a hunting dog or a milk cow.' So might a Finn have read in 1792. Values change; but the contemporary sportsman will esteem skis even more highly for recreation than his ancestor did for his vocation. Skiing is a part of the heritage of the Finn and its associated motions and movements are bred in him. His prowess in it, regardless of other considerations, has enabled him to make another form of impact beyond his home country.

## A Season of Sociability

Winter used to be very much the season of sociability. It was a time when opportunities for outdoor work were reduced; but it was a time when facilities for movement were transformed. Winter as a season of mobility was presented to the English in the *Atlas Maritimus* in 1728 – the first significant compilation printed in England to cover the geography of Finland. With the arrival of winter, it was recounted [35],

'. . . the inhabitants look abroad . . . to travel and carry on their needful affairs, and without troubling themselves about night or day, sea or land, rivers or lakes, dry land or wet, the face of the world being all smooth and white, they ride on their sledges . . . carrying a compass with them for the way, wrapt in warm furs for the weather and a bottle of aquavita for their inside, with needful store of dried bread and dried fish for their food.'

Winter fairs were an essential part of the season of sociability. Those of the northland were invested with an early reputation. Olaus Magnus wrote of 'the icy marts . . . of all the northern peoples'. Over two hundred years ago, James Thomson made the winter fair a part of his narrative poem, *The Seasons*.

> Even in the depth of polar night, they find
> A wondrous day – enough to light the chase,
> Or guide their daring steps to Finland fairs.

Brooke saw 'the long cavalcades of Laplanders and reindeer going northward' after Kängis fair (12–16 December), 'the great point of union for the whole of the northern Laplanders'. The most impressive seems to have been that of Åbo, held from 20–23 January. It attracted visitors from all parts of the country. They were a source of great interest to Edward Clarke, who identified Russian traders, with their 'dark lamb-skin caps of a peculiar kind of curled wool . . . dragging after them their hand sledges'; Ostrobothnians, whole families of them, walking beside their horse-drawn sledges, their contents covered over with fishnets: Laplanders and Savolaxers, with frozen game, fish and venison haunches brought unimpaired to market, though they might be several months old. The distances that these visitors travelled impressed Clarke greatly. It was as though Scottish islanders made a sleigh journey to Sussex.

Winter journeys were made in response to church festivals. At Tornio, Brooke reported 'the surface of the river crowded with Finland peasants . . . on their return from attending divine service.' Yrjö Kokko has a more recent appreciation of the Christmas service at Karesuando [36]. But it was left to Edward Clarke to produce a climax from Brändö in Åland, where he recorded [37]:

'Upwards of an hundred sledges, to which wild and beautiful horses were harnessed, (which) all took to the sea; where, being extended upon the ice in a long line of procession, they formed a most singular sight. If it had not been for the swiftness with which this vast retinue moved, it might have been compared to a caravan crossing the desert . . . We overtook them upon the ice, in full gallop . . . They had all taken their whet of brandy, as usual, after divine service; and the coming of strangers among them, at this moment, adding to their hilarity, such racing commenced upon the frozen main, as reminded us of antient representations of scenes in the Circus and Hippodrome.'

His lively sketch of the event even found its way into H. G. Bohn's *Handbook of Modern Geography* (1861) from where Victorian children must have obtained a somewhat unusual impression of 'Finns returning from divine service'.

Shrovetide was the old-fashioned climax of sleighing and tobogganing. There are the relics of scores of local customs associated with 'Shrovetide gliding.' Samuli Pauluharju has a pleasant record of it from Hailuoto in northern Ostrobothnia. 'They looked forward to Shrovetide as one looks forward to seeing the sun break through a gap in the clouds. Folk then had an excuse to go visiting and dancing, they tobogganed and they drove in sledges.' In many parts of the country, sleighing was accompanied by noise and by incantations. In Loimaa, Satakunta province, the drivers 'tied as many bells and other tinkling gear as they could find . . . to their harness' – so, too, in Valkeala (Karelia) and Virtasalmi (Savo) [38].

In much of the Finnish countryside, social visits are still more common in winter than in summer. But the transformation of Finland from an agricultural country to an industrial country and from a nation of country dwellers to a nation of urban inhabitants has modified its social rhythms. As with the people of Western Europe at large, most Finns treat summer as the time of relaxation.

Yet there are moments in the winter when special ski trains and ski planes set off on their daily shuttle to Lapland, when the scores of ice rinks in Helsinki swirl with floodlit skaters, when the mammoth rallies of *Suomen Latu* are under way that it might be agreed with Thomas Milner from a hundred years ago that 'winter is the busiest season of movement'.

## The Nature of Lumbering

Winter is also the busiest season of movement in another way. It is the harvesting time for Finland's principal crop – the coniferous woodlands. Timber is the foremost asset of Finland. In terms of value, three-quarters of its total exports consist of forest products which are mostly manufactured. A considerable part of the rural population is occupied by lumbering – felling, cutting and transporting trees. At the time of the 1960 census, 112,000 or six per cent of the total gainfully employed population of Finland, drew the bulk of its earnings from forest work. In many communes of central and northern Finland, the figure exceeded a third, while in the whole county of Lappi, it rose to about 12,000 or 12 per cent of the total rural gainfully employed. A still larger part of the rural population has lumbering as its main secondary activity. Summer farming and winter lumbering are naturally complementary pursuits.

Until the ground freezes, until the ice has cast bridges over lake, coastal inlet and bog, and until the snow has covered meadow, swamp and rock outcrop with a thick blanket, the runners of the sleigh cannot bear the forest worker easily to the felling areas. The arrival of suitable snow and ice conditions is, therefore, watched with some anxiety. The best lumbering winter will have a sufficiently hard frost to freeze the bogs and fens before the first snow falls. It will have a snow cover which is thick enough but not too thick, which forms early and which lasts long into the spring. If snow falls on unfrozen ground (and this is not infrequent), it is disadvantageous. In the south especially, such conditions give rise to all sorts of inconveniences. For example, sledges cut through the ice of bogs and swamps so that their logs may have to be unloaded and reloaded. The best lumbering winter will also be free of excessively low temperatures. Given such conditions as those in 1965–6, operations frequently cease – partly because tractors cannot function in very low temperatures.

The winter ways to the felling places used by horse and sledge usually follow property boundaries. Shorter cuts across bogs, lakes and rivers (sometimes actually along river courses) aid directness of access. Winter ways used by caterpillar tractors have to be broad and they must also be cleared of the larger stumps and boulders. Those used by wheeled tractors have to be levelled to such a degree that they are not true 'winter roads'. Extensions of the road net may be made by pouring water on to the surface of the bogs and thereby producing a road bed of artificial ice. Such tracks are true winter roads.

While the snow and ice cover are still the *raison d'être* of winter softwood movement, the character of forestry operations is changing. Mechanization proceeds apace. Winter lumbering has its high season in January and February. A peak employment of 200,000 men and 40,000 horses was reached some ten years ago, but today only about 125,000 men and 20,000 horses are employed. The trees to be felled are marked in the summer and autumn preceding the felling season. Although felling and hauling proceed to a large extent simultaneously, the main part of the felling tends to take place in the beginning and middle of the winter and the main part of the hauling in late winter and early spring. The use of motor saws has reduced the need for lumbermen; while the use of tractors and trucks has had a proportionately greater effect on the number of horses needed. In the state forests, some 6,000 motor saws were employed in January 1965 as against only 2,600 in January 1958. It is estimated that in the lumbering activity conducted under the State Forestry Board there were 1·5 men per motor saw in 1964, against 3·5 men in 1959. In West Finland, the corresponding figures were 1·6 men in 1964 and 5·1 in 1959; in Peräpohjola-Lappi, 1·2, 2·5. The number of horses bred in Finland has diminished so rapidly in recent years that forest economists fear a shortage of horses for lumbering in the relatively near future. One reason for the continuing need of horses is that a fifth of the timber-producing area is so dissected and rocky or boulder-strewn that neither tractors nor trucks can operate easily on it.

The State Forestry Board estimates that in 1964–5, 61 per cent of its timber haulage was done by either tractors or trucks, whereas in 1960–1, their combined share of timber haulage was only 35 per cent. West Finland, where distances are shorter and horse-haulage more advantageous, is exceptional in that horse-hauled timber still predominates. In this region, horses still undertake 69 per cent of the total haulage of logs and 61 per cent of the pulp wood.

At the end of the winter lumbering season, with the break-up of ice on river and lake, floating starts. In anticipation, pulpwood and logs are piled on to the ice of the lakes and bigger rivers. Bundle floating has largely replaced loose-floating and the weight of the timber in the bundles may be so heavy that water has to be poured on to the lake-ice to strengthen it. Today, only the lakes and bigger watercourses are significant for floating. Timber transport on the lesser waterways has been taken over by tractor and lorry. This has been made possible by improved mechanical facilities for constructing forest roads. Over 10,000 km. of forest roads have been constructed in the last twenty years. They have changed the direction, speed and monthly rhythm of timber movement.

There are elements of both constancy and change in the picturesque but hard life of the lumberman. In northern Finland, extension of settlement into the forested areas through state-supported colonisation schemes has made available a new pool of locally situated labour. This has somewhat reduced the demand for migratory labour. Nevertheless, in 1964–5, only 63 per cent of the winter workers in the State Forests of the Peräpohjola district of Lapland lived in the parish where they were working. Rather more than a third were from other parts of the country and occupied winter camps. As forestry becomes an increasingly skilled activity, the accent on seasonal labour tends to decline.

With the adoption of new techniques for felling timber, and of transport for moving men as well as logs, it is in the interests of the State Forestry Board and large private forest companies to try and recruit a more permanent corps of efficient labour and to attempt to even out seasonal demand. For all large scale timber producers, the mid-winter peak of employment and mid-summer trough becomes less pronounced. In the camps of the State Forestry Board, 26,000 men were employed at the peak of January 1957; 14,000 in January 1964.

A direct result of this tendency is depopulation of the winter camps (see Figure 22). At the end of January 1965, only 304 out of the 809 winter camp dwellings owned by the State Forestry Board were inhabited; 122 out of the 235 caravan units. The figure represented a substantial decline in the percentage occupied in 1963–4.

## The Virtues of the Winter Circumstance

The historic seasonal division of labour persists over most of Finland, if not among most Finnish people. Finland continues to turn winter to good use in its principal area of wealth – the softwood forests. It has a residual interest in the wild pelteries (though it is forced to define with increasing rigour the hunting season for such valuable fur-bearing animals as the marten, ermine and otter), and in the fisheries from beneath the ice of sea and lake. In time of national crisis, Finland has capitalized upon a deep understanding of winter terrain and upon a talent for moving over it. Indirectly, ice and snow have given rise to a variety of distinctively winter industries – from the large-scale, such as icebreaker construction, to the small-scale, such as the manufacture of sports clothing; from the mechanical, such as the foresters' mobile saw units and winch hauling devices, to the animal, such as mink farming, which takes advantage of low temperatures to encourage good fur production. The development of a winter tourist industry for foreign visitors is perhaps the most sophisticated expression of trading in winter. Finally, not a little of the country's physical exercise and mental relaxation spring from winter circumstance. Snow hill, snow castle and snowman, sleigh, ski and skate belong to the earliest impressions of childhood. It speaks volumes for the degree to which Finland has accommodated itself to the restraints of its high latitude that the adult world has so much time and energy in its modern economy for playing with winter.

## BIBLIOGRAPHY

[1] Mss. in Valtion arkisto, Helsinki.
[2] N. G. af Schultén, *Själfbiografiska anteckningar, mss.*, Åbo Akademi Library.
[3] H. Tegengren, *En utdöd lappkultur i Kemi Lappmark*, Åbo, 1952.

[4] A. Hämälainen, *Hylkeenpyynti Keskisen Pohjanlahden suomenpuoleisella rannikolla*, Helsinki, 1929; G. Ehnholm, Sälfångsten i våra skärgårdar, *Skärgårdsboken*, Helsingfors, 1948.

[5] H. Smeds, *Malaxbygden*, Helsingfors, 1935.

[6] O. Wetterhof, *Färdmännen på Bergö*, Stockholm, 1887.

[7] J. Sundfeldt and T. Johnson, *op. cit.*

[8] A. Kivi (Tr. Alex Matson), *The Seven Brothers*, London, 1929.

[9] R. Travers, *Letters from Finland*, London, 1911.

[10] U.T. Sirelius, Über das Jagdrecht bei einigen finnisch-ugrischen Völkern, *Memoires de la Société Finno-Ougrienne*, 33, 2 and K. Donner; Quelques traineaux primitifs, *Finnisch-ugrische Forschungen*, 15, 91–104; T. I. Itkonen, Finlands fornskidor, *På Skidor*, Stockholm, 1936.

[11] A. Dillon, *A Winter in Iceland and Lapland*, London, 1840, II, p. 196.

[12] P. du Chaillu, *The Land of the Long Night*, London, 1900, p. 60–1.

[13] The standard statement from the northern countries is G. Berg, Sledges and wheeled vehicles, *Nordiska museets handlingar*, 4, Stockholm, 1937. cf. also R. Ahlbäck, Folklivsstudier, *Suomen kulttuurihistoria*, II, Helsinki, 1945, Vol. 300 and G. Grotenfelt, *Det primitiva jordbrukets metoder*, Helsingfors, 1899.

[14] A. Dillon, *op. cit.*, II, p. 176.

[15] C. Linnaeus, *op. cit.*, II, p. 211.

[16] *Kalevala.* (Tr. William Kirby), London, 1907.

[17] William Coxe, *op. cit.*

[18] Edward Clarke, *op. cit.*, XI, p. 240.

[19] A. de Capell Brooke, *op. cit.*

[20] There is a fine example in Borgå museum.

[21] K. Vilkuna, *Vanhat veto-ja ajoneuvot*, Helsinki, 1930.

[22] Communication from Professor Gösta Berg, Skansen, Stockholm. 1872 is the earliest reference according to Fil. Lic. Göran Rosander of Uppsala.

[23] Communication from O/Y Joutjärvi, Lahti.

[24] K. B. Wicklund, Ur skidans och snöskons historia, *På Skidor*, Stockholm, 1928, 5–86; Mera om skidans historia, *ibid.*, 1929, 252–79; U. T. Sirelius, Über einige Prototype des Schittens, *Journal de la Societé Finno-Ougrienne*, 32, 30, 1913; T. Itkonen, Finlands Fornskidor, *Suomen Museo*, XVIII, 7–16; XXXV, 80–88; Fennoskandia-skienes oprinnelse, *Festskrift til Rektor J. Qvigstad*, Oslo, 1928, 77–87.

[25] T. Itkonen, *Suomen kielen suksisanastoa*, Helsinki, 1957.

[26] *Kalevala*, (Tr. F. P. Magoun Jr.), Runo. 13, p. 77.

[27] Mrs. Alec Tweedie, *Through Finland in Carts*, London, 1897.

[28] J. Acerbi, *op. cit.*, p. 250–1.

[29] G. A. Gripenberg, Om skidlöpningens betydelse i militäriskt hänseende, *Finsk Militär Tidskrift*, 1887, VII, 467–75.

[30] A. E. Nordenskiöld, *Vegas färd kring Asien och Europa*, I, II, Stockholm, 1880–1.

[31] F. Nansen, *The First Crossing of Greenland*, London, 1890.

[32] See V. Balck, *Illustrerad Idrottsbok*, E. Collinder, Skidlöpning, Stockholm, 1886, 1–34; H. R. Sandberg, *Den finska Skidan i arbetets och Idrottens Tjenst*, Helsingfors, 1893; Contributions by J. Kirjavainen to *Hiihtäjä*, 1955, 135–54; 1959, 115–26; 1958; 147–84; D. M. M. Crichton Somerville, E. C. Richardson and W. R. Rickmers, *Ski-Running*, London, 1904.

[33] J. F. Regnard, *Voyage de Laponie, 1681*, Paris, 1875.

[34] Communications from O/Y Esko Järvinen A/B and Urheiluaitta.

[35] *Atlas Maritimus et Commercialis*, London, 1728.

[36] *The Way of Four Winds*, London, 1954, 123–5.

[37] Edward Clarke, *op. cit.*, XI, 253–4.

[38] E. Enäjärvi-Haavio, *The Finnish Shrovetide*, Helsinki, 1954.

# 6      The Balance Sheet of Winter

Winter is an inconstant phenomenon. Because Finland is more affected by it than most countries, even minor changes in the character of winter will have exaggerated consequences. Accordingly, it is fitting to consider longer term cyclical changes in the duration of winter, as the opening theme of this chapter. A second, and complementary, theme is the changing mental attitude to winter. This is partly but not wholly related to the changing technical circumstances which make life more comfortable. The change in attitude is both a cause and an effect of modifications in the traditional seasonal rhythm of activity – the third topic of this chapter. Changing climate, changing attitudes and changing rhythms of activity are all relevant to any formula for assessing the costs of winter. But unlike heating, lighting, transport and clothing, they are not readily reducible to financial terms. The pessimist will aver that winter cannot be forgotten even in summer, for as with most territories in high latitudes, Finland suffers the risk of summer frosts. The optimist will always find sufficient brightness in the brief summer to proclaim its victory over winter.

## The Changing Character of Winter

Besides irregular variations from year to year, winter also shows cyclical variations in intensity and duration [1]. Evidence for these longer term variations is limited by the availability and reliability of records. While temperature and precipitation data for the last hundred years are reliable, those for more than a century ago are not wholly dependable. Cyclical variations in the severity and mildness of winter tend to have importance for Finland for two reasons. First, so much of

Finland's plant and animal life is already upon the margins of its natural habitat. Secondly, Finland is more conscious of the impositions which it suffers through winter than are most countries.

All records seem to indicate that, by comparison with the later nineteenth century, a general amelioration of the climate has occurred in the northern hemisphere in the twentieth century, with the 1930's showing a peak improvement. For Finland, the most pronounced temperature increases have occurred in November–January, April–May and July–August. February has provided little reliable evidence of positive change and March has shown less pronounced improvement than most other months. More precise evidence has been examined for the period 1934–8. During these years and by comparison with the average for the period 1901–30, the length of the thermic winter (i.e. when the thermometer stands below o°C.) shortened over the greater part of the country by 24–27 days; in the Åland islands and Kainuu province, by 29 days; in the south-east and in the area north of Oulu, by 16–22 days. Cyclical ameliorations in climate would seem to result from variations in the strengths of continental and maritime air masses. During the period 1934–8, the improvement in Finland's climate was especially noticeable in April and May, November and December. The change is significant because spring weather conditions are critical for the maintenance and development of Finland's flora and fauna.

The amelioration, which has been accompanied by a somewhat stronger westerly element in the annual wind rose and by a measurable increase in the salinity of Finnish coastal waters, has been sustained; though it has not been so continuously pronounced as in the 1930's [2]. Zoological responses have been more noticeable than the appreciably slower botanical adjustments.

Bird watching has become a popular pastime in Finland as in other countries. It has been particularly rewarding over the last thirty years. Bird populations tend to show three developments – an increase in the variety of permanent residents, alterations in the movement of weather migrants, changes in the distribution of native species. There are, in addition, modifications in the movements of summer migrants, but they are independent of changes in winter's régime. Among bird indicators of winter improvements are the tawny owl (*Strix aluco*), the bluetit (*Parus cæruleus*) and the crested tit (*Parus cristatus*). All have been immigrant and expanding in Finland in the last three generations. Bluetits are especially sensitive to hard winters, because their food requirements can only be met from a limited range of buds during the restricted daylight hours. For weather migrants, the improvement of late winter/early springtime temperatures has a threefold effect. Firstly, it encourages earlier arrival; secondly, it favours earlier nesting; thirdly, it prompts a broader distribution. Among birds that have responded to the earlier disappearance of winter conditions are weather migrants such as the rook, starling, blackbird, lapwing, black-headed gull and moorhen. The starling (*Sturnus vulgaris*) has proved a remarkable indicator, arriving soon after temperatures rise above o°C. A century ago, the starling arrived in south-west Finland in mid-April. For the last generation, it has appeared at the end of March. The springtime appearance of the white wagtail has changed similarly. In response to the milder springs, resident native birds, such as the 'southern' chaffinch and the boreal bramling, have shown a distinct northward shift in their zones of concentration [3]. At the same time, the populations of more northerly bird species have diminished in more southerly areas. Given higher autumn and lower winter temperatures, the song thrush, reed bunting and redwing are among the increasing number of birds that tend to overwinter in south-west Finland. The recurrence of a hard winter can have severe consequences for newer residents such as the blackbird.

Changing winter conditions are also reflected in the numbers of game creatures [4]. Two principal types of game are identified – farm game (partridge, pheasant and field hare) and forest game (capercaillie, grouse, ptarmigan and snow hare). The succession of mild winters in the 1930's favoured a particularly pronounced increase of farm game both in numbers and expansion in distribution. Winters of heavy snow and severe cold such as 1939–40, have a decimating effect on game, because their food supplies are found principally beneath the snow cover. At another level are the reactions of *Lepidoptera* to shorter and longer cycles in the duration of snow cover. Butterflies in the pupa stage are very sensitive to severe autumn or spring frosts when the ground has no protecting cover of snow.

Among the lesser predators, the polecat (*Putorius putorius*) is also a sensitive indicator [5]. There are fossil finds of its skeleton from warmer periods in the past; while polecat furs were listed in early Finnish trade returns before the harder winters set in. Subsequently, it virtually disappeared and only made a reappearance in the 1860's. At the beginning of the century it began to spread powerfully and by the 1930's was encountered as far north as 63°. The polecat and the tawny owl (with the climatic responses of which it is closely associated) prey chiefly upon small rodents and frogs, both of which are difficult to obtain in winter. As a result, the polecat has a habit of seeking the vicinity of human settlements in winter, where the chances of finding mice and rats are higher. The catch of polecats fell sharply in harder winters such as 1939–40, 1940–1 and 1941–2.

Changes in the character of winter have become popular subjects for speculation by both students of history and natural history [6]. Increased mortality and especially long winters are correlated to the extent that early spring rather than November ought to bear the Finnish epithet 'the month of death'. When failures to adjust to environment are quoted as causes affecting the course of Finnish history, it is necessary to reflect upon the contemporary reverse of the coin. Accumulated human achievements have done much to account for the twentieth century success of Finland's struggle with a cold climate. But these achievements may not have had the same result if the country were living in the climatic environment of the eighteenth century.

## The Changing Approach to Winter

The changing approach to winter is a reflection of changes in technology. But a new mentality was required before the new possibilities and opportunities that they offered could be adopted. A century ago, many Finns in the north and the interior conformed to the description of Bayard Taylor:

'In the long, long winter when there are but four hours of twilight to twenty of darkness – when the cows are housed, the wood cut, the hay gathered, the barley bran and fir bark stowed away for bread, and the summer's catch of fish salted – what can a man do, when his load of wood or hay is hauled home, but eat, gossip and sleep? To bed at nine and out of it at eight in the morning, smoking and dozing between the slow performance of his few daily duties, he becomes at last as listless and dull as a hibernating bear . . . The tropics relax, the poles benumb.'

Such a reaction was despised and rejected by Zachris Topelius. Winter, he protested, was intended for more than sitting on the stove [7]. His arguments in favour of a fuller and more useful employment of the winter season were fair if it could be assumed that Finnish men and women had sufficient food to produce the energy required to accept winter's challenge. To stay on or by the stove and to take life easy were ways of conserving heat and energy – as they were in much of Europe during the years of near starvation of the Second World War.

Zachris Topelius, reflecting upon the seasonal round in his *Twilight Tales* (*Sägner i Dimman*), put a new appraisal into the mouth of Consul Rönnevall. It merits quotation.

'Speaking as a merchant, I could call (winter) an enemy, because he shuts up our harbours and breaks off the two great regulators of our balance of trade – export and import . . . But winter can also be called a friend, even a business man's friend . . . building his bridges over ice and snow . . . (Finland) produces in summer, but gathers together, puts in order and makes up its accounts in winter. Half of the country is a wasteland in summer, but it comes to life with the first frost and the first snow . . . and when the sun shines on the blinding snow, twelve hours' work must be done in six.

'Winter is the element for which we are born. Take winter from us and we would no longer know ourselves, we would be rootless creatures between a southern people without the south and a northern people without the north . . . Nature may be a club to bludgeon us, but we have skulls of iron . . . Winter may be the denial of summer's light, warmth and organic life, (but) the whole of winter's sociable life is a protest against this denial . . . Winter, in denying the outer world, opens up new inner worlds. In summer we are forced to live for the earth, in winter we are free of it.'

It was not only a philosophy for winter living that Topelius put forward, but a new aesthetic appreciation of the winter landscape. He saw a whole rainbow of colour in winter's snow and ice and besought the country's artists to go out and paint on to their winter canvases all the colours on their palettes. Nor did he forget the colours that illumined winter's darkness – the Aurora borealis. Winter darkness was undeniable and inescapable; but, for Topelius, 'all darkness was not night'. It was natural that Topelius, the poet, should be lyrical about winter. His youthful *Winter Song* (*Vintervisa*) from 1844 is the most representative of his feeling.

> Smidig skida skön
> över slätten slinter.
> Vacker är vår vinter,
> Och så frisk är snön.

Plenty of ordinary people enjoyed similar flashes of winter exhilaration. Edward Clarke recorded one when he met [8]

'Brilliant skies; horses neighing and prancing; peasants laughing and singing – "Fine snow! brave ice! brave winter!" Merry-making in all the villages. Festival days, with unclouded suns; nights of inconceivable splendour and ineffable brightness; the glorious firmament displaying one uninterrupted flood of light, heightened by an *Aurora borealis*, while boundless fields of snow reflected every ray.'

But few Finns could forget for long the threat of famine associated with winter and the harrowing uncertainties of life and limb. Topelius's attitude to winter could hardly assume a more popular character until the community in which he lived enjoyed a personal security comparable at least with his own. The greater security that began to show itself towards the end of the nineteenth century infused a new gaiety (or a new romantic gloom) into verse and song.

In the meantime, artists heeded Topelius and re-examined the colours of winter. Winter had features that appealed to the imagination of the primitives, romanticists, realists and expressionists alike (but only, of course, if society could afford artists). Winter was popularized in art. It gleamed in the photographic likenesses of Helsinki's back streets under Magnus von Wright's sugar candy snow; it entered the narrative canvases of Albert Edelfelt. It was diversified by Axel Gallén-Kalela in his broad panoramas of the north country, in his monumental settings for the Kalevalan heroes, and in his cosy snow-clad Ruovesi cabins. It was satirized by Hugo Simberg. It was endowed with a new luminosity in Pekka Halonen's gentle snowscapes from his home parish of Tuusula. It was given a new discord in the harsher and rougher interpretation of Aimo Kanerva. Winter has many moods. How strange to find environmentalism coming full circle and a contemporary Finnish art critic declaring [9]:

'When it has hardly begun, our summer sinks back into shadow and night. The sombre dark surrounds us, mixes with the painter's colours and by its cold tranquillity, restrains his brush.'

People have always had time in the Finnish winter. They have not always had energy. Once they had energy to play with winter as distinct from merely existing through it, the change in attitude could be mirrored in many fields. However, once Finns began to migrate to cities and to shut themselves up in factories, the white winter world became an escape.

Popularization of the attitude to winter is inseparable from professionalism in the national treatment of it. Dealings with winter are increasingly the task of the specialist. In Finland's advanced society, experts are constantly searching to see how science can be more effectively wedded to art. Winter is an area in which the rewards of this exercise have been rich.

## *Winter and the Seasonal Rhythm of Activity*

Writing of Finnish conditions in the early years of the nineteenth century, N. C. af Schultén declared that 'a day's work in summer is dearer than ten days' work in winter'. The values reflected the varying seasonal demand and supply of labour. When men work closely with nature in temperate and high latitudes the pattern of activity in winter differs considerably from that at other times of the year. Schultén's values no longer hold; but, since a substantial proportion of Finland's labour force continues to be engaged in agriculture and forestry, seasonal rhythms in climate persistently affect short-term demands for labour.

The farther that Finland advances from primary production in a limited range of commodities to diversified manufacturing industry, the less fundamental is the disturbance caused by winter to labour input and industrial output. Winter conditions have little effect upon the day-to-day operations of most manufacturing plants. Partly as a result of this, input of labour units (expressed in thousands of man-months) for Finland at large shows an increasingly even monthly distribution [10]. The minimum figure is encountered in July – historically one of the months of maximum labour input, but in the contemporary industrial economy, the leading holiday month.

Figure 26 illustrates the rhythms of employment for 1961–4 in three different sectors of the economy and juxtaposes the rhythm of unemployment. It shows clearly that the sag in winter demand for labour still causes a moderate increase in unemployment. The degree of unemployment differs regionally as well as within the different sectors of the economy. Figure 27 sets the national scene for the year 1964. It reveals that the absolute volume of unemployment is greatest in those employment districts where the total labour force is largest, but it conceals the fact that winter unemployment tends to be relatively greatest in the north and east where winter is hardest and longest. The statistics refer to registered unemployed and, therefore, omit the considerable amount of concealed winter unemployment. In rural communities, especially, there is much winter under-employment.

Winter unemployment is reduced directly by improved domestic planning as well as indirectly through changes in the structure of the economy. Three areas of improved planning may be mentioned. First, the demand for labour in farming

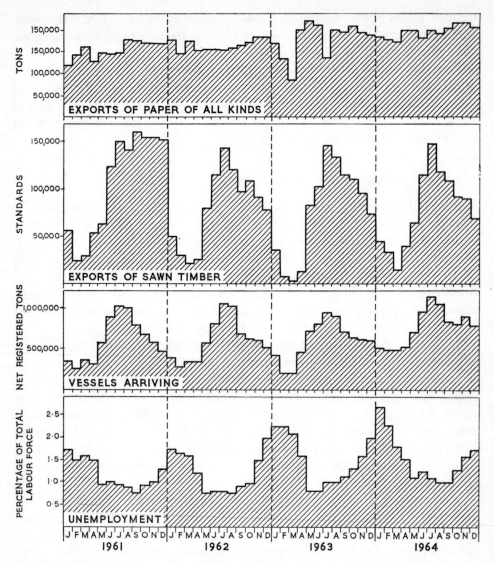

**Figure 26. Monthly Rhythms for selected Finnish Economic Activities 1961–4**

(Based on the returns of the *Bank of Finland* Monthly Review)

and forestry is increasingly stable. While the great migrations of winter forest workers continue (see Chapter 5), they are smaller than hitherto and are organized with growing care. Secondly, the casual employment of dock labour in the seaports most susceptible to freezing has been succeeded by work programmes that take account of winter's exigencies; though an unexpectedly hard winter may throw several hundred men out of work in southerly harbours such as Pori. Thirdly, major changes are taking place in climatically sensitive industries, such as building and constructional work. It will be recalled from Chapter 4 that the

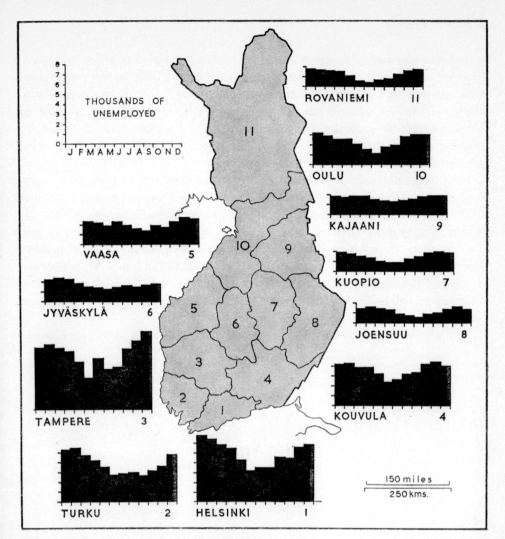

**Figure 27. Monthly Registered Unemployed
for Finland's Eleven Employment Districts in 1964**

(Based on material supplied by the Finnish Ministry of Communications and Public Works)

technical restraints on winter building are being reduced. But while new techniques enable year-round continuation of operations, they impose extra costs which contractors and constructional companies are not always prepared to absorb. To reduce seasonal unemployment in the building industry, which may be exaggerated by cyclical disturbances in the labour market, investment may be initiated by the Ministry of Works and state loans may be extended to local government authorities for winter building.

Since 1961, Finland has been divided into three areas for the purpose of state-supported building operations [11]. The areas have been defined largely according to the duration of winter. Thus, without a special permit from the central authority, state-supported work may not begin until 1 October in Area 1 (which consists of the employment districts of Helsinki, Turku, Tampere and Kouvola). The date is advanced to 1 August in Area 3 (Lapland) and to 1 September for the rest of the country. All state-financed schemes must be set in motion before February and all building schemes must be halted on 1 June. Authority to operate outside these times may only be given at cabinet level.

While winter interferes with outdoor activity inside Finland, it also disturbs

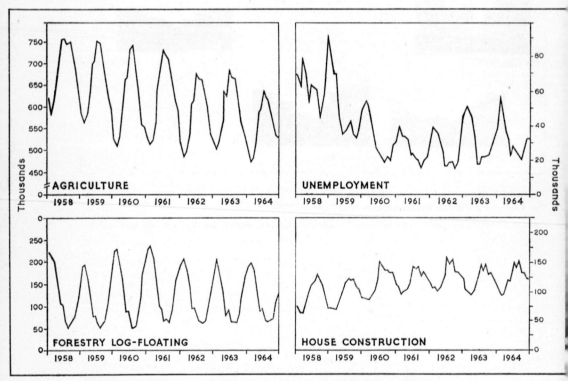

**Figure 28. Rhythms of Employment for Three Different Sectors of the Finnish Economy, 1958–64**

The diagram also juxtaposes the rhythm of unemployment for the same period.
(Based on material in *Työvoimakatsaus,* 1965)

Finland's external relations. A pronounced seasonal rhythm of international trading persists, with the winter decline transmitting its effects to the labour market. Figure 26 illustrates three rhythms of trading activity for the years 1961–4. The graph of monthly unemployment is set beside them. The variation in amplitude between summer and winter trading figures differs greatly for different commodities. As has already been hinted, exports of raw materials tend to have a greater seasonal variation than exports of manufactured goods. The winter decline in the export of sawn goods, pitprops, sleepers and telegraph poles is persistent. One reason for this is that these exports move mostly from gulf head ports, which remain difficult of access in most winters. A second reason is that they are of low value in proportion to bulk and cannot withstand the same transport costs as more valuable processed products. The resulting trading oscillations are only slightly less exaggerated than, for example, those of the 1930's.

Figure 26 shows that the export of paper products traces a completely different monthly distribution from that of sawn goods. Largely for reasons of raw material supply, Finland's principal paper and pulp plants grew up away from the most favoured locations for winter trading. The relatively steady flow of their exports is partly an expression of the ability of paper and pulp to bear higher freight charges. In winter their products are generally moved by rail to the nearest open harbour. The steady flow of paper exports is also explained by the nature of the demand. Customers insist increasingly upon regular deliveries of paper and pulp. Finnish exporters must guarantee a regular supply or they will suffer from competitors who are able to conform to market requirements. Figure 29, prepared by Auvo Säntti from statistics for 1948, provides a precise example of the winter movement of exports by rail from the stations of Kemi, Oulu and Toppila to Finland's west coast harbours [12]. Since the cost of the rail haul represents a substantial tax on profits, it is not surprising that attempts are made to find a loophole. It would seem logical in an ideal world for the mills in southern Finland to supply export markets in winter and for the mills tributary to the northern half of the Bothnian coast to deliver their goods during the period of open water.

Winter affects the flow of trade of interior as well as of coastal producing centres. Figure 30 provides a good illustration of the seasonal trading adjustments of the inland softwood centre of Kajaani in north-eastern Finland (Kajaani exports both sawn timber and processed softwood products). It is based on railway statistics for 1963. These are assembled for four monthly periods and do not distinguish different commodities. The result is nevertheless a good illustration of the effect of winter on commercial life. Figure 30 shows that Oulu serves as the leading export harbour for Kajaani, with Toppila (to the immediate north of Oulu) as the second. Shipment is concentrated during the second half of the year, that is during open water. It will be recalled from Chapter 3 that Oulu is usually closed until well into May. The actual figures for movement from Kajaani to Oulu were 3,000 tons, January–April; 178,000 tons, May–August; 98,300 tons, September–December. The shipment of goods from January to April is so small

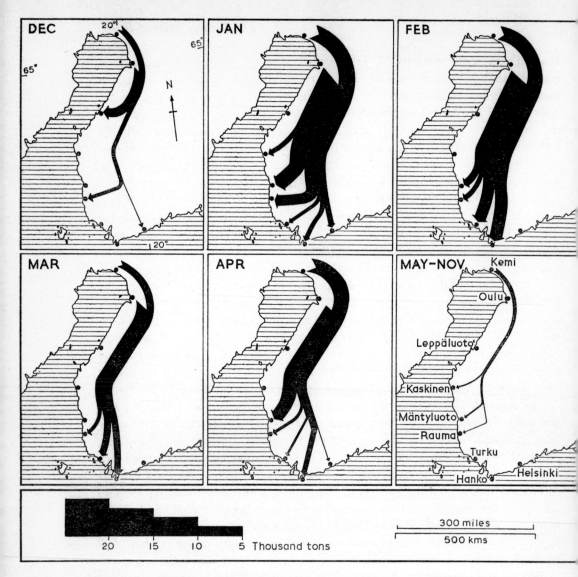

**Figure 29. A Flow Diagram of Cellulose Exports during the Winter Navigation Season 1948**

The diagram employs waggon-load statistics moving south from the railway stations of Kemi, Oulu and Toppila. (Source: Auvo Säntti, *Publications of the Turku Geographical Institute*, 25, 1952)

**Figure 30. Seasonal Trading Adjustments in 1963 for the Inland Softwood Centre of Kajaani**

Statistics refer to commodities moving by rail and are prepared for four-monthly periods – January to April, May to August, September to December.
(Based on materials supplied by the Statistical Department of the Finnish State Railways)

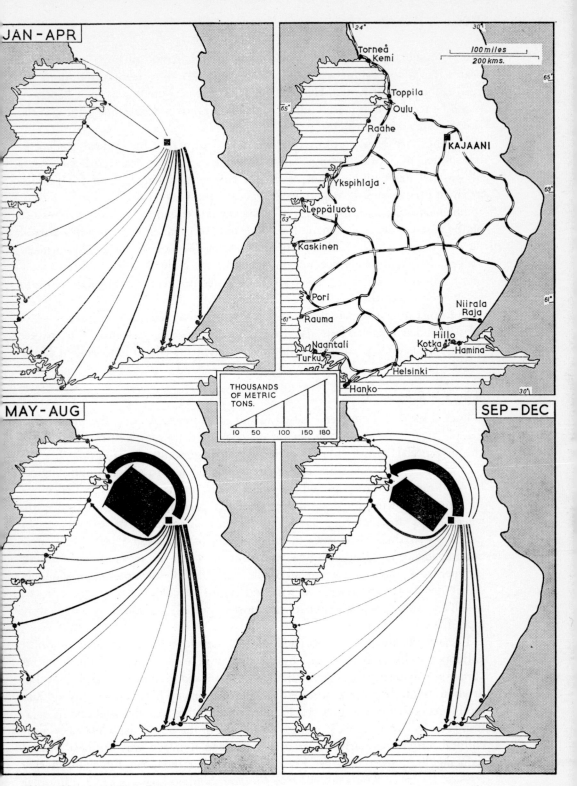

JAN-APR

MAY-AUG

SEP-DEC

Torneå
Kemi

Toppila
Oulu
Raahe

KAJAANI

Ykspihlaja

Leppäluoto

Kaskinen

Pori

Rauma

Niirala
Raja

Hillo
Kotka
Hamina

Naantali
Turku

Helsinki

Hanko

100 miles
200 kms.

THOUSANDS
OF METRIC
TONS.

10    50    100   150   180

**Figure 30**

133

that it suggests a considerable stock-piling in anticipation of open water at the nearest harbours. Figure 30 also indicates a steady movement throughout the year to the ports of Kotka, Hamina and Hillo (near Hamina). From Chapter 3, it will be recalled that these Gulf of Finland harbours have become critical in the annual icebreaker campaign.

Finland's seasonal rhythms of trading are cut across by cyclical tendencies transmitted by world trading. These movements ease or exacerbate the effects of seasonal fluctuations. Thus, a decline in international demand for Finnish products exaggerates the negative effects of winter. Conversely, during periods of commercial expansion, the effects of seasonal change tend to be reduced. Pressure on the labour force and demand for goods may be great enough to shift a part of the productive activity to those months when the level of output would normally slacken. If exceptionally severe winter conditions coincide with a boom in the international market, the effects are transmitted to give a particular boost to production in April.

In former times, export sales as well as shipments sagged during winter. Today, sales are independent of seasonal circumstances, responding essentially to market developments and speculation. The flow of payments is also independent of the seasons [13].

## Winter in Summer

Winter does not altogether desert Finland in summer. Among the phenomena that plague the farmer and perplex the meteorologist are summer frosts [14]. They are an especial hazard in two periods – the beginning of springtime growth (i.e. when the temperature averages between 5°C. and 10°C.) and mid-August. Frosts during the former period are especially felt in the south-west, where crops are already growing in May; during the latter period, in the centre and north where crops are maturing late. The regional distribution of summer frosts indicates a maximum incidence in the provinces of Oulu and Vaasa, and a minimum incidence in Åland, Uusimaa and Mikkeli. There are two different types of summer frost–those of widespread occurrence and those of a local nature. Widely distributed frosts are associated with indraughts of cold polar air; local frosts, which are more sporadic in impact, are most commonly produced by temperature inversion.

Local frosts are closely associated with the development of stagnant air which is trapped in lower-lying tracts. Forest growth in areas of quite modest contour variation may also prevent free circulation of air and give rise to conditions that promote frost. There is a sufficiently close relationship between swampland and local frost occurrence to give rise to both local weather lore and scientific speculation [15]. In *Kalevala*, frost was given a home in the boglands; while early agricultural writers regularly declared that bogland drainage was the best way of reducing local frost hazards. Frost is a recurring theme in Finland's literary classics. In Alexis Kivi's novel *Seven Brothers*, Sompio bog was drained in order

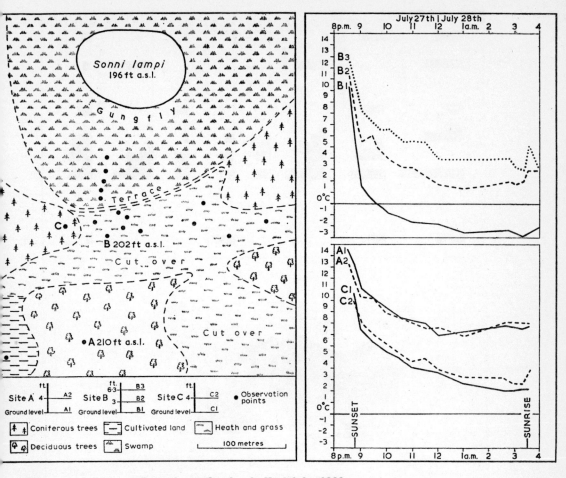

**Figure 31. A Summer Frost Investigation in Karislojo, 1880**

The left hand map indicates the type of terrain and the location of the thermometers. The right hand graphs show the temperature recorded by the thermometers indicated on the map.

(Based on Th. Homen, Nattfrostfenomenet, *Bidrag till Kännedom om Finlands Naturoch Folk*, Helsingfors, 1885)

**Figure 32** (*overleaf*). **Summer Frost Damage in Finnish Marks per Hectare of Cultivated Land, 1952**

The columnal diagrams illustrate the intensity and distribution of August frosts at some of the principally affected recording stations. Rate of exchange in Old Finnish Marks, £1 =890.

(Based on *Katokomitea*, Oulu, June 30, 1953)

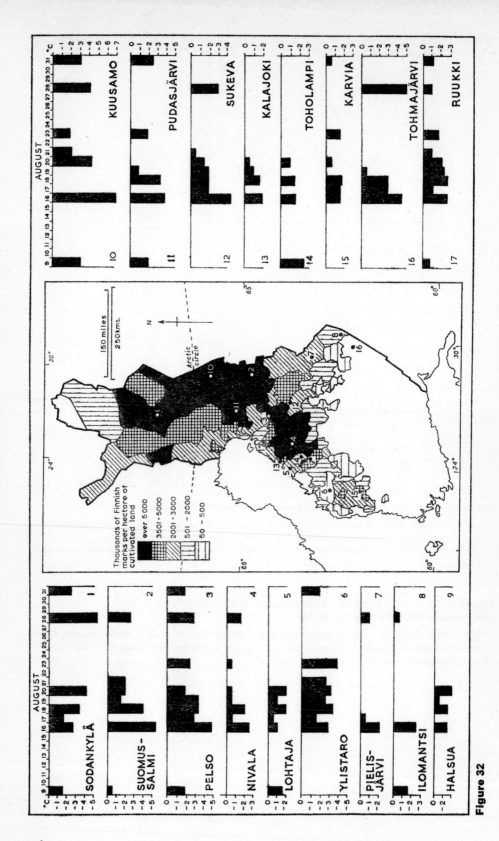

**Figure 32**

136

to dispel the threat of summer frost. Such a frost destroyed the scented ryefield at Impivaara. 'Like a grave, so cold and silent was the night, and on the bosom of the field, a grey frost lay like a choking nightmare.' The theme of the 'iron nights' recurs in Finnish literature. In his book of stories *Lastuja* Juhani Aho strings together winter titles from darkness (*Tervetuloa talvinen pimeä*), through the hard tail end of winter (*Taka talvi*) and spring cold (*Kevätkylmät*) before concluding with summer frost (*Idän halla*). No one has symbolized the grim spirit of summer frost more tellingly than Hugo Simberg whose painting is reproduced in Plate 5.

The first proformas for collecting agricultural returns, circulated by C. C. Böcker in the 1820's, included questions about the incidence of summer frosts and it is possible to reconstruct from them simple maps to show the regional intensity of its occurrence [16]. In the same context, Figures 31 and 32 are also historic statements. They illustrate local and national impacts of summer frosts respectively. Figure 31 reproduces what is probably the first example of local frost occurrence to be scientifically recorded. The diagram is reconstructed from observations made at Karislojo on the night of 27/28 July 1880. Figure 32 accompanies one of Finland's first full frost damage reports. It was compiled in 1953 and is based on commune returns.

A special committee of the Ministry of Agriculture (*Hallakomitea*) now centralizes information on the incidence of frost damage. Finnish farmers do not normally insure against frost, but a precedent has grown up for the central government to compensate those who suffer heavy damage. The number of farmers making claims rose to peaks of 98,000 in 1949 and 180,000 in 1962. It is not possible to compensate every claimant. Distribution of compensation takes place through officers of the regional agricultural societies, who must consider the circumstances of each farm affected. In the summer of 1964, for example, only a fifth of the compensation claimed was available for distribution. The most needy cases took precedence and larger holdings had to absorb their losses. On another occasion, in 1959, farmers who had suffered damage were allowed a reduction of interest rates on certain loans in lieu of direct compensation. In the light of these developments, frost damage reports have acquired a correspondingly professional form. They list individual crops (rye, wheat, oats, barley, mixed grain and potatoes), the extent of the damaged area in hectares, the expected harvest in kilogrammes per hectare and the estimated financial loss suffered.

Some attempt is made to outwit summer frosts with scientific acumen. Biologists breed plants that are frost-hardy: technicians devise frost-fighting apparatus. There are sulphur-vapour burners which produce a smoke cover to reduce radiation on clear nights when frost threatens. Within the area protected by their vapour, temperatures can be maintained from 3° to 7°C. higher than in surrounding unprotected areas. There are machines to stimulate air mixture and sprays to reduce frost risk. But all of these devices are costly to employ in terms of man hours and can only be afforded by intensive growers such as market gardeners and horticulturalists.

As farms are multiplied and the cultivated area is extended in districts that are vulnerable to summer frosts, the bill for frost damage tends to increase. In planning the extension of arable land, it is clearly wiser to avoid areas subject to summer frosts than to invest in large scale schemes of frost defence. In addition, where areas of marginal risk are involved it is also wise to select the crops that are least susceptible to damage. In this context, a relative frost risk index for different areas and for different forms of terrain has been proposed by Seppo Huovila [17]. It calls for the conduct of exact studies over extensive areas with a view to determining their relative liability to damage by frost caused by radiation. If the boundaries of areas sensitive to summer frost were satisfactorily defined, administrative action could be taken to discourage the growth of particular crops on them or to encourage their alternative use (e.g. reversion to woodland). In other words, farmers who insisted on planting frost-sensitive crops in areas classified as subject to frost risk, would not be compensated for any loss sustained.

There is an extreme hazard beyond the summer frost – the hazard that winter will not leave the land and that Finland will suffer an abbreviated Lapland summer of three months' 'green winter'. The essence of this exceptional situation is summarized in the map of the spring thaw for 1867 (Figure 6B).

## The Triumph of Summer

But summer does come – and usually triumphantly. By April, the heat of the sun gains in intensity. De Maupertuis wrote of it as a time of the year when 'There is summer in the sky, but winter on the ground'. Snow creeps down the roof tops, curls over the eaves and drips into curtains of icicles. The granite rocks sweat a crust of frost as the warmer air touches them. It is the time of the year when the shadows are white; for, in detail and at large, the snow disappears last from the shaded areas. The autumn-ploughed fields are zebra-striped with snow. Around tree stumps, boulders or rock outcrops, the snow retreats fractionally – though with gathering momentum – each day. And the local patterns of retreat add up to the country-wide withdrawal of the blanket of winter until, as Topelius expressed it in *Sampo Lappelill*, only Lappmark sits 'like a great white nightcap on Finland's high head'.

In the south, the first flowers – *Tussilago farfara* and *Hepatica triloba* – thrust through the dead brown grass. But for them, Finland looks at its most penurious as winter dissolves. The long light days stare through the bare branches. The ribs of the country seem to stick through its seared flesh. The melting snow has its own peculiar smell: so has the earth moistened by the first spring rain.

Snow melt on land is more swift and more silent than ice melt on water. It is also more swift than the thaw of soil. Snow melt on water rots the ice beneath its crust. The compacted snow of the winter ways and the tracks left by the pressure of the skis have always attracted the attention of visitors. Olaus Magnus observed that they 'remain like bridges' in the watery ice. Sea birds move back responsively from the edge of the sea ice to wade and flutter in the sloppy shallows around the skerries and islands. The ice melt is more impressive than the snow melt because it makes a more powerful aural impact. *Jäänlähtö* or *islossning*, the break-up of ice, is accompanied by pistol-like reports, by cannonadings and by deeply ominous reverberations before the final collapse and sinking of the ice-surface. The treacherously glazed surface rarely succumbs without a toll of lorries, cars, carts, sledges and pedestrians. (Hugo Simberg's symbolical painting, 'Death skating' epitomises these incidents.) The sudden liberation of waters, the crashing ice slabs, the ice jams on the inland waterways constitute a spiritual as well as a physical phenomenon. They spell the demise of winter.

Daylight lengthens until artificial lighting – even the guiding beam of the lighthouse – is unnecessary. J. V. Snellman wrote of 'the tropical strength' of growth in summer – from 'snowdrift to thick grass' may be 'but the work of several days'. If there was an element of exaggeration in his recollection from his home valley, there is plenty of meteorological evidence to substantiate his references to summer's powerful heat. Its temperatures are generated by the continental European high pressure which Finland shares. July maxima also force on powerful convectional thunderstorms. High temperatures and humidity encourage a rare surge of vegetative growth – and an exuberant insect life.

In the world of nature it is a time of great and concentrated outpouring of physical energy. Because of its brevity, summer is also a time of great expenditure of human energy. When Finland was predominantly an agricultural country, summer was a season of almost relentless labour. There was no night to bring to an end the working day, so that labour in the fields resulted in an over-employment of energy. Since most Finns no longer engage in farming, summer has become the season of relaxation. Even for the farmer there are summer periods of relaxation. For urban Finns, it is a time when life is lived out of doors and when city streets are emptied by the exodus from town to country. School holidays, extending from June to 1 September, reinforce the attention paid to summer. Summer burns its way literally and metaphorically into the memory of the visitor – in the virtual fetish of the tanned skin, in the wild berries (strawberries, raspberries, cowberries) which drip fiercely red and rival the colour of the scalded crayfish; in the high midsummer bonfires which mark with their flames the feast of St. John (*Juhannuskokko*) and in the terror of forest fires with their tell-tale plumes of smoke on the horizon. Although its triumph may be short-lived, summer revives and revitalizes the Finn.

## A Bill for Winter

It is tempting, if difficult and unwise, to try and translate the bill for winter into financial terms. In theory, it would seem that a statement of winter's account might be rendered by constructing a balance sheet for the principal items discussed in this book. A formula might be devised by adding the costs of protection against winter (heating, food, clothing, medicines) to the costs of the assault on winter (breaking the ice at sea, clearing the snow on land, lighting the darkness) and the costs of damage by winter (from highway and building damage to frost destruction of cultivated plants), and by subtracting from them the cost benefits that accrue from winter (sporting, lumbering and the stimulus to new industrial and technical enterprise).

A rough assessment of the cost of the winter of 1962–3 to Finland has been attempted by Seppo Sauri [18]. Figure 33 assembles his estimates diagrammatically. Two-thirds of the bill is made up of the costs attributable to heating, building and farming. Sauri's bill ignores the benefits that derive from winter; but this is excusable because, apart from the contribution to lumbering, they are less tangible. The astronomical figures of the bill are difficult to grasp. They make more sense if expressed in other terms. For example, if the costs estimated by Sauri are set against the value of Finland's gross domestic product for the year 1963, they are close to four per cent of it [19]. If they are reduced to a *per capita* figure, they amount to 152 new Finnish marks (*c. £*17) for each of Finland's 4,500,000 inhabitants. In these terms the estimate appears to err on the low side.

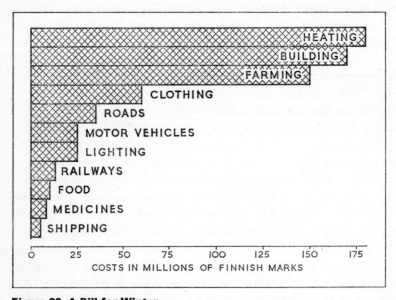

**Figure 33. A Bill for Winter**
The calculations are the estimates put forward by Seppo Sauri
for the winter of 1962–3

The *per capita* incidence of the bill for winter varies substantially from south-west to north-east Finland. Financial adjustments are made in recognition of this fact. The salaries of state employees (including teachers) are higher in the more inclement part of the country. Temperature conditions are included in the general assessment of regional handicaps [20]. For example, there are salary adjustments for state employees who live within the average annual isotherms −1°C. to 1°C., with extra relief for areas where the average annual temperature is less than −1°C. These 'cold climate' subsidies are made principally to offset the extra costs of heating and clothing. They are social controls brought into play to redress the balance between those who occupy the areas of greater and lesser stress in a universally hard environment. Such adjustments play an increasing part in regional salary differentials; though, because they figure as domestic cash transfers they do not enter the national bill for winter.

The approach to winter is dynamic. Consequently, the bill for winter tends to grow as resources available for spending on it increase. The appetite of winter grows on what it feeds. At the personal level, the standard of living has risen sufficiently for expenditure to shift with gathering momentum from necessities to extravagances. At the national level, expenditure on winter amelioration is increasingly a product of country-wide planning and co-ordination – a community expenditure for community benefits. In the international arena, when political and economic pressures decline to a minimum, so that Finland is able to employ a full quota of its capital resources and physical stamina to deal with winter, restraints fall to a minimum. In the perspectives of the polar world Finland's winter is a modest phenomenon; but the approach to it benefits to the full from all technical advances made for living in a cold environment. Finland shares with the rest of the Scandinavian states a reputation for technical, economic and social experiment. Its peoples are able to minimise the effects of a cold climate because they enjoy the combined advantages of an advanced technology, an affluent society and a welfare state.

# BIBLIOGRAPHY

[1] I. Hustich (ed.), The recent climatic Fluctuation in Finland and its Consequences, *Fennia*, 75, Helsinki, 1952; I. Hela, On the Periodicity of the recent Changes in our Climate, *Merentutkimuslaitoksen julkaisuja*, Helsinki, 1951, 149.

[2] S. Segerstråle, The recent Increase in Salinity of the Coasts of Finland and its Influence upon the Fauna, *Journal Conseil International pour l Exploration de la Mer*, 1951, 17.

[3] E. Merikallio, Der Einfluss der letzten Wärmeperiode (1920–49) auf die Vogelfauna Nord-Finnlands, *Proceedings of the Tenth International Ornithological Conference*, Uppsala, 1950.

[4] O. Kalela, Metsäkauriin esiintymisestä Suomessa ja sen levinneisyyden muutoksista lähialueilla, *Suomen Riista*, Helsinki, 1948, 3.

[5] O. Kalela, Hillerin levinneisyyden muutoksista Suomessa, *Suomen Riista*, Helsinki, 1948, 2.

[6] G. Utterström, Climatic Fluctuations and Population Problems in early modern History, *Scandinavian Economic History Review*, Stockholm, 1955, III, 1.

[7] Z. Topelius, *Föreläsningar, mss.* University Library, Helsinki.

[8] E. Clarke, *op. cit.,* p. 189.

[9] A. Krohn (ed.), *Art in Finland,* Helsinki, 1953, p. 96.

[10] P. Kukkonen, Seasonal Fluctuations in Industrial Production in Finland, *Bank of Finland Institute for Economic Research Publications,* Helsinki, 1961, 8.

[11] *Valtioneuvoston päätös,* Helsinki, 1961, 589.

[12] A. A. Säntti, Railway Traffic in Finland from Centres of Population to Export Ports in 1948, *Publications of the Geographical Institute of Turku,* Turku, 1952.

[13] V. Holopainen, The Seasonal Rhythm in the Finnish Exports of sawn Softwood, *Acta Forestalia Fennica,* Helsinki, 1964, 61.

[14] W. R. Mead, *Farming in Finland,* London, 1953, p. 35–9.

[15] M. Franssila, On the Temperature Conditions in a large *aapa* Bog Area in Finnish Lapland, *Central Meteorological Institute Publications,* Helsinki, 1962, 53.

[16] *Böckerska Samlingen,* I–III, State Archives, Helsinki.

[17] S. Huovila, On Precautions against Crop Damage due to Radiation Frost within hilly Regions, *Societas Scient. Fenn. Comment. Phys.,* Helsinki, 1964, 29, 4.

[18] S. Sauri, Mitä talvi maksa, *Suomen Kuvalehti,* Helsinki, 1964, 48, 3. A parallel exercise has been undertaken for Sweden by K. M. Savosnik, *Svenska Turistföreningens Årsskrift,* Stockholm, 1955.

[19] P. Grönlund, The national Income of Finland, 1960–65, *Bank of Finland Monthly Bulletin,* Helsinki, 1965, 39, 10.

[20] *Syrjäseutulisä-komitean mietintö,* Helsinki, 1956.

# Index

Aaltonen Oy., 105
Acerbi, Joseph, 111, Plate 3
af Schultén, C. N., 101–2, 119, 127
Aho, Juhani, 79, 137
alcohol, 98
Angervo, J. M., 41, 49
*Atlas maritimus et commercialis*, 20, 115, 120
Aulanko, 114
*Aurora borealis*, 126

bear, 86–7, 103
beaver, 103
Bergö, 103–4
birds, 38, 85–6, 123–4
Blüthgen, J., 29
Bohn, H. G., 116
Bothnian Gulf, 43–8, 55–70
Brooke, Arthur de Capell, 16, 18, 72, 101, 102, 106, 108, 111, 115, 116, Plate 2
Brändö, 116
building, 92–5, 128, 130
Böcker, C. C., 21–2, 41, 103–4, 137

Canada, 15, 32, 55, 59, 70, 112
Castrenianum, 25
Celsius, Anders, 21
Christmas, 79, 116
Clark, Edward, 17–18, 26, 39, 67, 90, 95, 103, 106, 114, 116, 126
climatic fluctuations, 122–4
clothing, 84–5, 95–7
consular authorities, 20
Coxe, William, 95, 100, 101, 106

Denmark, 15, 55, 61, 69
Dillon, Arthur, 105–6, 120
du Chaillu, Paul, 105, 111, 120
Duhamel, Georges, 19, 67, 83

Easton, C., 29
Eckerö, 17, 30, 53
Edelfelt, Albert, 126
elk, 86
employment, 127–31
Enso Gutzeit, Oy., 71
Esko Järvinen Oy., 114

fairs, 115–6
Fellman, Jakob, 105
ferries, 71
fishing, sea, 104–5, 111
– lake, 104
food, 97–8
footwear, 96, 97, 115
Forssa, 95
France, 20, 23, 61
fuel, 57, 89–91

Gainard, P., Plate 1
Gallén-Kalela, Axel, 126
Germany, 55, 57, 69
Great Britain, 14, 20, 21, 23, 53, 55, 56, 57, 61, 102, 116
Greenland, 112
grouse, 86, 124

Hailuoto, 116
Halonen, Pekka, 126
Hamina (Fredrikshamn), 34, 47, 61, 64, 68, 134
Hangö (Hanko), 23, 34, 54, 55, 64, 82
hare, 86
heating, 89–92
hedgehog, 85–6
Heinola, 105, 112
Helsinki (Helsingfors), climate, 30–2, 34, 36, 40
– heating, 90, 91, 92
– icebreaker construction, 58–9
– lighting, 79, 81
– shipping, 48, 54, 61, 64, 68
– snow clearance, 72, 73, 74–6
– winter building, 94
– winter unemployment, 129–30
– winter sports, 112, 117
hibernation, 84–7
Hietalahti (Sandviken), 58–60
highway clearance, 72–6
Hillo, 134
Homén, T., 139
Honkanen, M., 90, 99
horses, 98, 102, 118
hunting, 102–5
Huovila, Seppo, 138
hydro-electricity, 79–81
Häme (Tavastland), 105, 109, 112
– museum, 79
Hämeenlinna (Tavastehus), 114

Impilahti, 112
Inari, Lake, 31, 87, 105, 114
insulation, 92, 94, 97, Plate 13
Ilomantsi (Ilomants), 36
Ivalo, 33

Jaakkima, 112
Joensuu, 34
Johansson, O. V., 13
Joutjärvi Oy., 109
Jurva, Risto, 24, 26, 44–7
Jyväskylä, 34, 114
Jämsä, 114

Kainuu, 123
*Kalevala*, 12, 106, 108, 110, 120, 126, 134
Kajaani (Kajana), 38, 129, 131, 133
Kanerva, Aimo, 126
Kankaanpää, 115
Karelia, 20, 103, 105, 109, 110, 116
Karesuando, 116
Karislojo (Karislohja), 135, 137
Kaukopää, 71
Kemi, 61, 64, 68, 73, 131, 132
Kemijoki, 80
Kemijärvi, 71, 73, 109
Kivi, Alexis, 104, 120, 134
Kilpisjärvi, 34, 36
Kiuruvesi, 106
Kokko, Yrjö, 20, 116
Kokkola (Gamla Karleby), 68, 109, 113
Kotka, 34, 36, 47–8, 61, 64, 68, 106, 134
Kouvola, 129, 130
Kumlinge, 18
Kuopio, 25, 32, 40, 78, 63, 113
Kuusamo, 113
Kymijoki, 78
Kyösti, Larin, 102
Käkisalmi (Kexholm), 112
Kökar, 48

Lahti, 33, 109, 113, 115
language, 24–5, 27, 110
Lapinlahti, 109
Lapland, 72, 87, 98, 111, 113, 114, 117, 118, 138
Lappeenranta (Willmanstrand), 112

# Index

Lapps, 30, 41, 87, 96, 98, 102–3, 105, 110–11, 114, 115, 116
Lecke, Johan, 21
*Lepidoptera*, 124
lighthouses, 81–2
lighting, 78–82, 94
Linnaeus, Carl, 21, 87, 106, 108
Lloyds, 56
logging camps, 88–9
lumbering, 117–8, 130, Plate 12
lumberjacks, 88–9, 117, 126

Malax (Maalahti), 102
Manamajärvi, 70
Mariehamn (Maarianhamina), 40, 54, 57
Marine Research Institute, 23, 67, 68, 69
Maupertuis, P. L. M. de, 17, 18, 26, 138
Merikanto, Oscar, 115
Mikkeli (St. Michel), 88
Milner, Thomas, 117
Ministry of Agriculture, 137
Mono Oy., 105
Muonio, 40
Mäntyluoto, 55, 64

Naantali (Nådendal), 90
Nansen, Fritjof, 53, 112, 121
naval expeditions, 20, 23, 52–3
Nordenskiöld, A. E., 53, 112, 120
Norske Veritas, 56
Norway, 15, 37, 69, 71, 73, 87, 109, 112, 113, 114

Olaus Magnus, 15–17, 70, 78, 79, 104, 111, 115, 138
orchards, 36–7, 137
Orimattila, 112
Ostrobothnia (Pohjanmaa, Österbotten), 20, 103–4, 106, 107, 110, 111, 116
Oulu (Uleåborg), 22, 31, 36, 40, 61, 70, 73, 78, 92, 94, 106, 110, 112, 113, 114, 131, 132, 134
Ounasvaara, 113
owl, 123

Pekkanen, Toivo, 28, 49
Pallastunturi, 114
Palosuo, E., 50
Paltamo, 111
partridge, 86, 124
Paulaharju, Samuli, 116
Pekkarinen, Maja, 98, 100
Peräpohjola, 118–9
polecat, 124
pollen analysis, 105, 109
Pori (Björneborg), 55, 64
postal services, 19–20, 53, 107

Porvoo (Borgå), 114
proverbs, 29, 32, 39, 97
Päijänne, Lake, 71

Quarken, 20, 45, 53, 73

Ramsay, Henrik, 11, 69, 82
Rautalampi, 106
Regnard, J. F., 112
Reima-Pukine Oy., 105
reindeer, 39, 87, 103, 106, 114, 115
Riihimäki, 109
roads, 76–7, 83
Rovaniemi, 31–3, 36, 40
Rukatunturi, 113
Runeberg, J. L., 15
Russia, 53, 59–60, 61, 64, 74, 102, 105, 106, 114, 116

Saarijärvi, 106
Sandberg, Hugo, 110
Saimaa, Lake, 70–1, 73
Salpausselkä, 113
Satakunta, 116
Savo (Savolax), 20, 109, 116
Sauri, Seppo, 140
Schefferus, Johannes, 87, 111
seals, 103–4, 106, 114
Shrovetide, 116, 121
Simberg, Hugo, 126, 137, 139, Plate 5
Simojoki, H., 29, 49
Sirelius, U. T., 105
skiing, 20, 21, 97, 102, 109–17
Skiöldebrand, A. E., 17, 26, 47, Plate 4
Sköldvik, 90
sleep, 78, 83
sleigh, 102, 105–9
Snellman, J. V., 139
snow blower, 75
– melter, 75
– ploughs, 73–5
– shoes, 112
Sodankylä, 21, 33, 38
soils, 41–2, 76
Sortavala, 112
*sparkstöttning* (*potkukelkka*), 108–9
squirrel, 87
starling, 123
State Forestry Board, 118, 119
Stockholm, 21, 54, 64, 74
stoves, 98–90
summer frosts, 134–8
*Suomen latu*, 113, 116
Suomenselkä, 33, 88
Suomen Trikoo, 97
Suursaari (Hogland), 106
Sweden, 15, 53, 55, 59, 61, 69, 73, 87, 94, 105, 108, 109, 112
Säntti, Auvo, 132, 313

Tampere (Tammerfors), 73, 79, 94, 130
Tapiola, 91
Tavaststjerna, K. A., 54, 89
Taylor, Bayard, 19, 96, 125
Thomson, James, 18–19, 115
Tegengren, H., 103
thaw, 76–8
– ing techniques, 70–1
Topelius, Zachris, 23, 79, 125–6, 138
Toppila, 131
Tornio (Torneå), 17, 18, 23, 102, 108, 110
Tourist Society of Finland, 112
trade, 131–4
Travers, Rosalind, 104
Turku (Åbo), 17, 48, 55, 105, 115, 130
Tuusula, 126
Tweedie, Mrs. Alec, 110
Tyrnävä, 112

United States of America, 53, 59, 70
Uppsala, 17, 21
Urheiluaitta, 114
Utsjoki, 21, 31, 33, 34
Utö, 33
Uusikaupunki (Nystad), 111
Uusimaa (Nyland), 111, 134

Vaasa (Vasa), 53, 103, 104
Valkeala, 116
Veitsiluoto, 71
Viborg (Viipuri), 16, 64, 79, 90, 106
Vimpele, 114
Virtasalmi, 116
von Buch, Leopold, 98, 100
von Wright, Magnus, 126, Plate 6
Värtsilä-Koncernen Oy., 58–9

Widegren, Gustaf, 110
War, Winter (1939–40), 21, 51, 70
– Continuation (1941–44), 70, 90
– Museum, 113
winter sports, 112–5
wolf, 87–8, 103
wood fuel, 90

Ykspihlaja, 48
Ylitornio (Över Torneå), 96

Åland (Ahvenanmaa), 17–18, 29, 30, 33, 38, 39, 103, 106, 116
Åland Sea, 43, 45, 53, 69
Åström Oy., 105

Ödman, Samuel, 29
Öresund, 69